GOD'S HEAL+H CARE

Anchor to a Plan That Never Fails

DR. DANIEL ELEUTERI

Cover Design by 100Covers.com
Interior Design by FormattedBooks.com

ISBN 978-1-7352376-1-9 (Paperback)
ISBN 978-1-7352376-0-2 (eBook)

DEDICATION

This book is dedicated to my wife. You supported this wild idea to write a book that honors God. You have been my support through this journey. You are my rock!

For Jack. That you always know that you are God's child. That He is your healer and your provider. Stay young at heart and always pursue God in all you do.

Jesus looked at them and said, "With man this is impossible, but with God all things are possible."

—Matthew 19:26

CONTENTS

INTRODUCTION

Rise up; this matter is in your hands.
We will support you, so take courage and do it.

Ezra 10:4

Welcome to God's healthcare movement! I am so excited for you to begin taking the proper action steps to not only building your health but doing it in a way that pleases God. With so much "health" advice out there today, it can become challenging to navigate the path. Let's go on the journey together. Let me help guide you in a way that is biblical and based in truth of how our bodies were designed, God's design. If you put in place even some of what we discuss, you will see your health reach levels you never knew possible. Not because this book is full of gimmicks and tricks; it is not. It is, however, loaded with principles that do not fail. Let me say this, as much as these principles will never fail; you may fail them. That's alright. Do not be discouraged. Life will give us ups and downs; the goal is to remain as close to on track as possible. This book will help you to toe the line of "perfect" while giving you some grace. The more you stick with and implement these principles, the better you will become.

Here is what this book is not: It is not a panacea for all your diseases and health problems. As we have seen repeatedly throughout the years, we have all become so entrenched about finding "the cure" for everything, spending more time and money on the "thing" or drug that will finally take care of all our health problems. Here's the problem, we continue to see skyrocketing healthcare costs, more approved medications that allow us to keep living the same way, and what do we get? More of the same health issues. More cancer, heart disease, adolescent sickness, chronic health conditions that we have not seen before at the alarmingly high rate we see them. So, if you are one of those people who want the easy way out with a "pop a pill" mentality, I hope and pray that you continue to read this book and begin to shift your mindset to what real health is and where it truly comes from. Here is what this book is about: It's about finally bringing God back into this world. It is about anchoring to His laws and principles of how our bodies are created. We see more sickness and disease and forget that we were created in an image of perfection. Yet, we quickly dismiss this knowledge and take what the world gives us. We continually look for answers that God has already given to us; we want to ignore them and hope we do not become a statistic of failing health.

As a husband and father of a young son, I have found that my health has become much more important. If I am not actively pursuing health, it will not just appear to me; it will not just happen. Our world has become broken and sick because we have stopped pursuing God in every aspect of our lives, even in our health. We have seen this world hit us hard, and we have put all our faith into humans and into a healthcare system that has not led us to become healthier. We are allowed to believe we are healthy because we have an abundance of medication that makes us feel good, now. They help manage a symptom, for now. But is that what God wants for you? More medication and managing your health?

I have been a natural healthcare doctor, chiropractor, and Christian for well over ten years. I have taken care of thousands of people just like you. When I first see a new patient, they all want the same thing, to feel better, to be healthier, and not end up like everyone else, sick with more drugs! When they go through the processes I discuss in this book, they undoubtedly improve their health. It happens all the time, as long as they do what is necessary. Every time, they get well. So, what do you want with your health and your life? With your family's life and health? People get healthier because they come off medication, lose weight, and exercise, not because I hold a secret, but because they get back to how God made them. They anchor to Him in all things in all ways.

This book will help guide you back to putting God in the middle of your healthcare based on laws and principles that God has given you. You will get practical knowledge that you can use day to day and can implement immediately. Here's the thing: it isn't necessarily groundbreaking, earth-shattering knowledge you need; it is, however, necessary to take what you will learn and apply it. As you read, you will see that by implementing God's healthcare, day by day, little by little, you will find His grace extending to you even in your health. My prayer is that each person who reads this book and shares it with their family will put into place the healthcare system that

God approves of, the one He designed. When I pray for people and their health, I do not usually ask God to take away their health problems (sometimes I do), but I pray that they begin to follow more closely to Him and begin to put their health ahead of other things. I pray that they eat better, that they begin to think differently, and that their health outcomes match up with truly getting healthier. You are too important to too many people to forget about yourself and neglect your health. Now is the time to start getting excited for your life and living in abundance, especially when it comes to your health! You have been given the gift of life. Join God's healthcare movement. Let us honor God by living in a way that others want to emulate. Let us become the focus of health and be leaders in a world that has left God out. Let the way we live show the world that bringing God back into this world, even in our daily health, is what people want. I pray that you pursue God more and pursue your health more. You will begin to see dramatic health improvements as you put into place God's healthcare, a plan that never fails.

I promise, if you put into place the action steps I discuss in this book, you will see a massive transformation in your health. You may have tried everything else with little or no results, but this plan is one that will last, that you can pursue daily and see results almost immediately. There are no gimmicks, no quick and easy fixes, only direct, long-lasting effects. I have found, over the years of caring for people, that the normalcy of this world overtakes their minds. They have a problem seeking God in their health because they don't have to; they get comfortable with where they are. This mentality ultimately leads to poor health outcomes. Throughout this book, we will look at how to overcome these trials so that you can fulfill God's purpose in your life and live a life with abundance.

The only thing that will hold you back from pursuing God's healthcare is you. If you're a Christian and want all the goodness that God has for you in your life, then begin immediately. Do not wait and pray about getting healthier. Do not ask your priest or pastor. Do not wait for a sign from God to smack you in the face. Now is the time to get healthier. Now is the time to pursue God's healthcare.

Now that you know these things,
you will be blessed if you do them.

John 13:17

And every work that he undertook in the service of the house of
God and in accordance with the law and the commandments,
seeking his God, he did with all his heart, and prospered.

2 Chronicles 31:21

Whatever you do, work heartily, as for the Lord
and not for men, knowing that from the Lord,
you will receive the inheritance as your reward.
You are serving the Lord Christ.

Colossians 3:23-24

But be doers of the Word, and not hearers only,
deceiving yourselves.

James 1:22

*So whoever knows the right thing to do
and fails to do it, for him it is sin.*

James 4:17

Let's get started.

CHAPTER 1

A BROKEN SYSTEM
IN A BROKEN WORLD

You are from below; I am from above. You are
of this world; I am not of this world.

John 8:23

Before we begin, we need to get one thing straight: God not only wants you to be healthy but He also NEEDS you to be healthy.

So, how do you think you and your family are doing when it comes to being abundantly healthy? Do you feel that you could be doing better? Do you believe that you are doing the best you could be doing? Maybe your health is not that much of a priority, at least not right now. Is your health something that you know you need to work on but just haven't put it on the front burner yet? Or maybe you and your family are doing pretty well, and your health is somewhat of a priority.

Let's take a big picture view of the state of our healthcare. How do you see our healthcare system doing in terms of not only getting people healthy but keeping them healthy and living an abundant, God-centered life? Too often, it seems as if we are very optimistic in terms of our health, yet when we look at the state of our healthcare as a whole, we become quite pessimistic. We like to think that what we are doing as individuals is good, maybe even excellent; we are doing just fine. But then, in the same breath, we say that our healthcare system is terrible, it's so expensive, and all they do is medicate you! So, something seems to be off. More than likely, you are making your circumstances more improved compared to what is actually happening with your health. Why do I say this? Let's look at the statistics of our current healthcare system, and you can see for yourself how we are doing when it comes to being healthy and, more importantly, living a full, abundant life that God wants for us and desperately needs for us.

- U.S. ranks 37 in overall health.
- U.S. spends the most money annually on healthcare ($11,000+ per person) or $3.6 trillion.
- Near the bottom for infant mortality = 5.9 deaths per 1,000 births, compared to Japan, which has the lowest infant mortality of 1.8 per 1,000 births.
- Maternal mortality is among the highest in the developed world = 24 deaths per 100,000.
- Cancer affects 1 in 3.
- Heart disease affects 1 in 2.
- Diabetes is increasing in children.
- Obesity affects 1 in 3 (BMI over 30).
- Highest amount of prescription meds in the world.

- Lowest longevity, life expectancy is declining.
- Leading cause of bankruptcy is medical costs.
- Chronic disease at an all-time high.
- U.S. makes up roughly 5% of the world's population but take 75% of the medication of the world.
- Chronic disease is what the U.S. spends the most amount of money on, and according to the CDC, these are mostly preventable!

And the list goes on. Feel better?

Before we go any further, you need to understand that this list is happening to you and your family now! If you do not recognize that we are in a crisis, and you and your family are in an emergency, you are living like everyone else. We put ourselves into a happy bubble and hope nothing terrible ever happens. And worse, we try to ignore the fact that we are not pursuing health and just hoping that nothing happens. If we were all living with abundant health, then we wouldn't have the above statistics. If you're a Christian reading this, this should give you chills and should be polarizing how devastating a state we are in with our health. Look around you. Look at your family. The above list is happening to you whether you see it or not. It's happening for one fundamental reason. We have entirely removed God's perspective for our lives and our health out of this world and have relied on a failing, broken world to save us. Not him.

To better clarify this point, let's look at a common health issue. If you or your child had a fever, what would you do? You'd probably answer with something like, "Take a Motrin or Tylenol," maybe, "Take them to the doctor." Perhaps some of you would say, "Nothing, wait it out." I think most of you would freak out if you just "waited it out." We'll get there later, I promise. But all those answers are not right or wrong; they're just what we would do using our earthly perspective of our health. Right? If you were brought up with a particular belief system, that taking medication is the right thing to do, then you would take a drug. If, when you were younger, your mom had you rest and let it run its course, then that is what you would do. The point of this is to begin to understand that HOW we take care of our health is an enormous problem that has brought us to where we are today. It is the culmination of living in a society that does not take action toward health but will make every effort to avoid doing anything that would improve our health but, instead, take a simple way out for instant gratification. It makes sense. It's the easy way! It's the "feel good now" way! But as a Christian, focusing on what God wants for me and honoring how He created me, we must know that the simple way is most likely NOT the Godly way. Another example of a typical healthcare crisis is cancer. I know we have all experienced this in some way, whether personally or with someone close to us. What typically happens is they are living their lives the way they usually do, putting off things they know they should be doing and maybe have an odd symptom or find something on their bodies that wasn't there before. Perhaps a routine check-up finds something abnormal, and they go and have a test or a scan, and as the fear continues to build and the questions begin to mount, a diagnosis comes back. I will ask every patient who has had cancer, a heart attack, diabetes, or whatever may be the case, "Before this diagnosis, a week before, a month before, or a year before, how did you feel?"The overwhelming majority will say, "I felt fine." A lot of them, even after a diagnosis, will still say they feel fine! So now what happens? The medical model says to cut the tumor off, burn it off with radiation for weeks, and then a specific amount of chemotherapy in the hopes that the cancer will disappear. In the meantime, we are continually praying for a miracle. I think we've all had this exact scenario hit too close to home. We have all experienced this as a typical protocol for cancer patients. I am not saying that this type of care is wrong, or that it cannot help. But, I know you would all agree that in absolutely no way is that person getting healthier! Are you with me? In no way can removing an organ or poisoning an individual as much as possible without causing too much harm, actually be beneficial and life-giving. It may help shrink a tumor or even remove it. Praise God! However, more needs to be done if that life is truly going to be changed and given an "all clear" diagnosis. They cannot think for a second, once treatment is over, that they are free and healed. The work has just begun.If a person has a diagnosis of diabetes or high blood pressure, a similar cycle happens.They go to the doctor for their annual check-up, some blood work is drawn, and they are told what "normal" or "abnormal" is. If everything seems OK, they move on, assuming all is well and that they are as healthy as God made them, and nothing terrible will happen to them. If something is abnormal, they will do follow-up testing to confirm. If there is an abnormality, the next step is typically a medication or two or three. Taking medication allows them to think that they are healthy and that their abnormality is no longer an issue.

Does this all seem familiar? The point to take home is to understand that taking medication, in any dosage, is harmful to your body. There is no way that after taking a pill, you are healthier. Think about that. Are you healthier or are you just symptom-free? By living in this conventional healthcare model, we are allowed to believe that we are getting healthier because our symptoms have gone away or are under control. Do not take this the wrong way; in many cases, people need these medications to save their lives or give them a chance at living. The question then becomes, what are you doing to get to the cause of your health problems and not need medications? Most health-related issues are lifestyle-induced, and medications allow us to keep living the same way while our health slowly diminishes. Is this what God had in store for us?

Just to be clear, I would never tell someone just to stop taking prescribed medication. That's irresponsible. I say all the time, "What's the plan to get you off this medication?" In all the above scenarios—there are numerous other examples to use that follow a very similar path to a very similar outcome—not one of them leads to you, your spouse, your child, or your neighbor getting healthier. Are you with me on that? Your lack of symptoms does not equate to health. If that were the case, we would be the healthiest country in the world! We have been completely deceived into thinking and believing that because we have no symptoms or no diagnosis that we are completely healthy and free of sickness. This has allowed us all to live a lifestyle far from what God's wants and needs for us as we slowly move away from His purpose for us and move closer and anchor deeper to the deceptive nature of this world. It has to end. We need to gain control of our healthcare and not rely on what we've done in the past. It's not working. The only answer? Bring back God into your health.

Does that scare you, that to truly acquire health, we must let go of what we have always done? Be free of the shackles of continuous diagnoses, tests, and medication? Are you already questioning me? You should! I know that we all know that there has to be a better, more effective way toward health. The thought of having to take control of yourself and your actions is scary, especially when it involves your family and their health. I've never met an individual who wants more drugs and surgeries in their life. Not one person says, "Give me more chemo and radiation!" Why not? Fear. Pain. The unknown. More questions than answers. Fear is a strong captor. Practically everyone will pray for more health! "God, make me healthy! God bring a miracle to my life that removes this diagnosis!" That's a start. When God is more in the picture, and not further away, fear becomes more difficult to find. But just praying for a miracle and hoping God answers your prayer isn't enough in a fallen, destroyed world. There needs to be more. There needs to be faith in action.

It's All B.S.

No, I won't start cursing in the book this early on. It is all about your Belief System. So, what's your belief system on health, and does God play any part in it? If He does, is it a minor role or a starring role? Do you believe that He should play a role, or should we leave that up to the doctors? Maybe it is a combination of both. Again, there isn't a right or wrong answer, but if you genuinely believe in God and are a Christian, I think your response should be clear. If you know deep down that God needs to be more present in your health journey and not more absent, then the remainder of this book is for you. If you know there has been something missing from your health, and you crave for more in your life, then keep reading. God will show up big in your life and your health as long as we live by the principles He has given us to be healthy. I will bet if you're reading this, you know one or more people who have been struggling with their health for a long time. Perhaps they're Christians. I know it can be easy if they know God and know where they're going after they die to deal with failing health, but is that what God wants for them? To live a decent life, get sick, live with a chronic disease, and then die? I don't believe that a God who would send His son to die for them would be OK with them just being OK! Get them on this journey with you. It may change their life.

If you want more for your life, especially to truly experience God's abundance for you and your family, you need to have your health! If health hasn't been a priority in your life, now is the time to start making it a focus because God needs you to be well. There is good news if you've been struggling with your health, fighting an uphill battle, or just feeling lost and being pulled in every direction by the latest fitness craze or diet book or infomercial. The good news isn't always easy, but it is simple. Let's start moving away from this broken world and start getting back to God.

We will soon define what real health is so that you can take the proper actions in achieving health. The lack of actual knowledge of health has become a significant issue with our broken world, leading to a fractured, dysfunctional healthcare system. We have completely abandoned the principles of how God created us and have adopted a new identity in health that has brought us further from real health. We have entered into a healthcare crisis that leads us further away from who God has called us to be.

As I write this, I don't want you to think for a second that my family and I are perfect. We're not. Far from it. We've struggled with our health. We've lost family members to diseases and we will again. We don't live in a perfect world. We reside in a world that wants us to perish. We live in a world that finds delight when things go wrong. We are under constant attack from an enemy that wants us to fail. This world is not a Godly world. He does not reside here. You need to invest the time and effort to be a healthy, whole, servant of God. Be who He needs you to be so that you can bring God back into this world. How many times have you been to church, or small group, or even just among friends when a prayer request has been about someone or a group of people needing a miracle to get their health back? I know that, more often than not, prayers are for the sick, suffering, and dying. Let's be clear, we're all going someday, but HOW we go and WHEN we go are largely, in a way, up to us. I hope you understand that. I'm not saying that freak accidents don't happen; they do. I've been there, and it is awful. I'm not talking about that. I'm focusing on not living out our full God-given journey to bring His love back into a sick and dying world that no medicine or procedure can cure. Only more of Him will bring Heaven to Earth.

Have you prayed this prayer? "Please, God! Take this pain away! Remove this cancer! We need a miracle!" God is the God of miracles. I would suggest continuing to pray those prayers; people need them. Prayers work. God can cure someone in an instant! I pray those prayers over my family, friends, and myself practically every day. My sincere prayer is not to need to pray for a miracle in your life or your family's life. My prayer has always been that my patients, family, and the world start taking back control of their life, their health. Get on fire for God's love. Be addicted to move closer to His love and to move in His direction based on His principles that govern our health. If we did that, we would all be healthier, happier, and full of life to exude to the world that our God is for us.

Imagine your church, pastor, town, and family ridiculously healthy, and living the life that God has indeed called them to live. No sickness. No diagnosis. No obesity or need for medications or doctor visits three times per week. Just massive health and energy. Life would look a lot different. We are far from that vision. But it doesn't mean that it can't happen. It just starts with you knowing that God has a purpose for you. He wouldn't have wasted a second putting you on this Earth if you didn't.

Too often, we get so caught up in the pattern of this world that we forget who we are and whose we are. How easy is it to just fall back to the path of least resistance? This rings especially true to how we act toward our health. Remember that God called you. He called you to be great. Regardless of your current circumstance, regardless of your diagnosis, He is using you to show this black and blue beat-up world that we are His.

Let's put this into a health perspective. How many people in your sphere of influence are truly living healthy? Think about it. Maybe you thought of one or two people; perhaps it's just you.

But if I asked how many people you know who are not living a healthy, abundance-filled, God-centered, healthy lifestyle, how many would you say? More than half? The majority? The last question is, how many people *think* they're living a healthy, God-centered lifestyle? There is a difference. Like most doctors, one of the reasons I became a doctor was because I wanted to help people. My life was changed, my eyes were opened to what real healthcare is, and I thought the world deserved to know what health was. My goal was to start with myself and my family, then move to the next person and their family, and so on. It's a challenge, to say the least. People don't need a book or doctor to tell them that eating good food by God is right for them. They don't need someone to say stop eating Twinkies and drinking diet soda every day; or do they? What we all need is to stop looking for the next best thing in this world that will save us from disease, pain, sickness, and early death and look at what has already been done for us through Christ. We need to put His healthcare plan into action.

We must first quit blaming God for the lack of health that our lifestyle has created. Once we can understand that, we can begin to put Him back into our healthcare and use His system to live a healthy, abundant life.

How would things be different for you if you had an abundance of energy? What if you didn't need medications for a symptom or a sickness? Imagine feeling great so you can focus on your life and purpose. How would that change things? What if you feel pretty good now? I do. There's still another level of God's glory for you. There is always more. As we continue, we will understand the things that hold us back and what we need to do to gain access to being truly healthy and a closer version of who God needs us to be.

In John 8:23, Jesus says, "You are from below; I am from above. You are of this world; I am not of this world."

When Jesus speaks, we should listen. We've all heard this verse before, but it strikes a major chord with me when it comes to health. It may not be directly related to our physical health, but then again, it kind of does. The more we look around, especially in today's world, we can see that things are not right. But let's focus on our health here. We are continually looking for a CURE!!! Are we not? More money is being spent on something we haven't found. Does this make anyone else's blood boil? We have been bombarded with more drugs and treatments. We have learned to be incapable when it comes to taking responsibility for our health. Think about that. Because of all the information on "health," we have become paralyzed to what's real and what's not. What will bring us toward health and what's pulling us away? The world has done a great job breaking us down and making sure we know that our bodies are less than perfect and unable to be well. God knows how broken this world has become, but He wants so badly to be a part of our lives, and as a loving father, He wants us to be healthy.

Proverbs 4:20-22 says, "My son, pay attention to what I say; turn your ear to my words. Do not let them out of your sight; keep them within your heart; for they are life to those who find them and health to one's whole body."

In John 16:33, Jesus says, "These things I have spoken to you, that in Me you may have peace. In the world, you will have tribulation, but be of good cheer, I have overcome the world."

Proverbs 3:7-8, "Do not be wise in your own eyes; fear the Lord and shun the evil. This will bring health to your body and nourishment to your bones."

Exodus 15:26, "He said If you listen carefully to the Lord your God and do what is right in his eyes, if you pay attention to his commands and keep all his decrees, I will not bring on you any of the diseases I brought on the Egyptians, for I am the Lord, who heals you."

SUMMARY-TAKE 5

- Our healthcare system is not working, and you are in it.
- We live in a broken world that wants you to fail.
- We must bring God's healthcare plan into our lives.
- Quit blaming others (even God) for your lifestyle choices that have put your health where it is now.
- Build a genuine desire to seek God in your health.

But first, it is time to separate yourself from your current state of health.

CHAPTER 2

YOU ARE NOT YOUR DISEASE

It is for freedom that Christ has set us free.
Stand firm, then, and do not let yourselves be
burdened again by a yoke of slavery.

Galatians 5:1

So often, when a patient comes to see me, they'll use the phrase, "I have cancer." Or they complain, "I have arthritis, diabetes, neck pain, headaches." Or they'll announce, "I had a heart attack." They'll name their diagnosis and link it to themselves, as it is a part of them. It's theirs. When we do this to ourselves, we give very little hope of ever being free of it. Even when we get the diagnosis, the doctors say YOU have cancer, or YOU have diabetes. YOU had a heart attack. It drives the point home that YOU are sick. YOU have a problem and that the doctor needs to fix you. So, we begin the process we spoke about earlier. The medical treadmill starts.

Very rarely will someone who has been diagnosed with something tell me that their doctors gave them an actual health plan. Usually, it's more of the same. Take this medication this many times, and in so many weeks, we'll retest and see you again. Not one thing related to getting healthy is offered, but just reduction of a symptom, hopefully.

We end up on a dangerous and slippery slope that doesn't lead with much hope. We begin to feel stuck and scared like we're wandering in the dark without a flashlight. Even those close to us suffer. But this world has given us very few answers for the long term, the health outcome we are praying for. We just sit, waiting for a chemical to cure us! It sounds crazy, but isn't that what we do? We are praying to God that a drug, chemo, or radiation gets us healthy? Again, if that's the route you're taking, great; pray those prayers. God needs to be present in that. But don't you think there should be more?

As we go through a treatment plan to hopefully remove this symptom and save our life, there is very little we do ourselves to help our bodies build health. We become our diagnosis. Waiting for a pill to work has become one of the most significant issues that we face in terms of our health. We have become sick people. We have removed God from our lives enough to believe we are sick. We need a literal miracle to help save us. We are bound to this broken system, and this broken system has shackled us mentally to all but paralyze us from doing anything different.

In the world of social media, it becomes very polarizing on how clear this point is. If someone becomes sick or their child goes to their doctor or hospital for a sickness, it's all over the Internet. We pray for them, for the pain to be taken away and health to be restored; it's what we should do in those times. However, the more we post about it and complain about it, the more we stay bound and imprisoned to this thing that someone else labeled us to have. We act as if. If you come from a "poor" family or, at least, your parents told you that they didn't have any money or couldn't afford something you wanted, what do you grow up thinking? You're poor! You act as if, even if it's not true. But it rings especially true with our health. We become that disease.

Remember, I've been saying that our healthcare system is broken. I don't think we need to fix it; we need to transform it. Trying to fix it gets us more of the same. Trying to make healthcare cheaper or more accessible, better medication prices, all-access payers, open market, private market, etc. It's all the same. Nothing is changing because the use of this system remains the same, and THAT is the inherent problem. No one is getting healthy; we just have fewer symptoms and more drugs. We become a society of legal drug users and never become unbound from the "need" of those drugs. We stay broken and helpless, and we continue to have a victim mentality.

It's essential to understand and always remember that we are in a broken, hurt world. The enemy is still out to destroy us. Often, we become such a shell of who we once were because of our lacking and failing health; we start to think that we aren't worthy of being healthy. We begin to tell ourselves that this is how our life is going to be, and we give up hope; we give up searching, and the hurt of the world captures another spirit to brokenness.

Have you ever blamed God for a disease or the loss of a loved one? I know I have. If you're a parent or grandparent, uncle, or aunt, or are close to your friends' children, you'll understand this. If my son is crying or in pain or even if he's upset about something, he will come to me and ask me to fix it. I wish it were that easy. I don't walk on water, and God is not a genie. When I tell my son not to do something, but he does it anyway and gets hurt, all I can do is be there to console him and hope he learns. We're all the same. We live a life that makes us comfortable, and we try to avoid all sources of pain to bring joy and gratification. We look for instant gratification and ignore any long-term consequences of our actions. We create a lifestyle that is not conducive to health and then blame God for our sickness! All He wants to do is take the pain away.

Are you ever around someone who has the most negative mindset? It usually transcends into multiple areas if not every area of their life. They just find themselves as the victim and play the blame game. Whether they're complaining about not having money, being in a bad relationship, or always being sick or overweight, whatever it is, they are unintentionally anchoring to a mindset that they are less than and unworthy of anything beyond their current situation. We start to feel sorry for them. Maybe we feel sorry for ourselves, and the cycle goes round and round, never taking responsibility or latching onto the spirit that God has given us.

We tend to turn to the Internet for hope. But this is as dangerous as eating an apple from a tree that God said not to eat from. When we look at everyone else's "perfect" life, we get quick confirmation that our situation is DEPRESSING! I will continue to mention the fact that we live in a world that God is not a part of; He does not reside here. We are up against a real enemy, lurking at every corner and wanting and willing us to fail. Our health is an easy target. Why? There is so much information and a general lack of actual healthcare practice that we fall so quickly into sickness. When we are comparing our lives to everyone else's (or the nice parts of it that they display), it becomes abundantly clear that we have no chance of gaining our health back or even living according to God's plan for our lives.

Has the thought of being unworthy in any area of your life popped into your mind? You see someone else living your best life, and you aren't even close to having what they have? I know it's crossed my mind, and if you're human and honest, it must have crossed yours. We begin to make excuses for ourselves, put others up on pedestals, and drop ourselves down into the dirt. We start establishing a dialogue in our minds to justify why we have what we have or lack what we desire and make it OK. "Well, the reason I don't have that house or that car yet is because my boss is selfish and a terrible leader and doesn't pay me enough." "They are truly blessed, look at what they have, God is watching over them. But I'm just lazy, and God forgot about me." We can justify just about anything in our minds, and it's quite impressive. We begin to make excuses for our situation. Let's be honest; it's all lies! God doesn't play favorites! As a father, He loves His children equally. He wants incredible things for all of us, regardless of what we've done or failed to do. I know I will look around and see other people doing great and working hard to find success. I can very easily fall into jealousy. It's hard to be happy for people, especially those you think deserve less than you! What if we were to set our eyes back on God and let Him be our only critic. Cut the

♠ ♦ Rules of Texas Hold'em ♥ ♣

- ◆ The betting starts after two cards are dealt face down to each player. These cards, called "hole cards", are unique to each player.

- ◆ The next three cards (called the Flop) are then dealt face up in the center of the table. These are community cards and are part of each active player's hand. A second round of betting occurs.

- ◆ The fourth community card (the Turn) is dealt face up in the center of the table, followed by another (third) round of betting.

- ◆ The final community card (the River) is dealt face up in the center of the table, followed by a final (fourth) round of betting.

- ◆ When all bets have been equalized, the showdown takes place among the remaining players, and the winner is declared. If only one player remains at the end of any round, there is no showdown and the pot is awarded to that lone player.

- ◆ A player uses the best five cards among his pocket cards and the community cards to determine his hand. That is, a player may use both, one, or none of the two hole cards he started with. (When none are used, the player is playing the board.)

- ◆ Check-and-raise is allowed in all Hold'em games (except on the first round, when a player, on his turn, must either bet or fold).

ties of our current state, especially our health, and re-anchor to His will for us.

We play out this scene nearly every day, and it runs particularly true for our health or lack of it. I see it all the time. People will say that I'm lucky for the lifestyle I live. That they could never work out or eat a certain way; that's just not them. They'll say they tried to live a healthy life, but it just didn't work out. It's incredible how we are all so similar. My favorite is when someone will come to see me after we had set a plan for better health, and a week later, they say it didn't work. I love it! You're telling me that after 45 years of gaining weight and being sedentary a week of 2% better didn't fix all your problems?! I guess you're right; you can't get any better. Are you kidding me!?

Let's play more of the blame game. It becomes so easy to fall back on the way we have done things for so long. It's the path of least resistance. Doing the bare minimum to survive without much pain is what we have learned to do. No one likes pain. No one enjoys feeling tired or sick. So, we end up doing the very least to get by with as little pain and suffering as possible. Over time, we again learn to become helpless in our own lives. We become OK with being OK. As time passes, that feeling of just being OK puts us in a position of feeling worse, being sicker. We end up further away from health and we become OK with that current situation. We, as humans, love to play this game. What happens next? We tell ourselves a story about why we are the way we are. We fall back on that path of mediocrity and put blame where it is necessary, on someone else or find other excuses. We, as humans, operate this way. I know; I have these same tendencies. I've just trained myself over time to realize what I'm doing and to course correct as soon as I can.

Who else can we blame?

I know! How about mom and dad? That's an easy way out. We so often will blame our current health state on our parents or grandparents. Are you overweight? Well, maybe your parents were. It must be your parents' fault. Have breast cancer? Grandma did too. It's her fault, and she passed breast cancer to me. Diabetic? Dad also had diabetes since he was forty. I knew I would get it. Family history of dementia or Alzheimer's? It looks like you're going to get that too. If I meet someone who has any of these diagnoses, by no means do I put them down or expect a change to happen over one conversation. Sometimes it does. But, in reality, it takes time to get back to understanding what health is and how to achieve it. When we have a health scare or are living in a chronic state of sickness or disease, we can very easily fall back to the most natural place to put the blame, and that's our family history or, as we call it today, genetics. Remember, this world is full of sick and suffering people. The point of this book is to not only give you hope but to give you a system to bring God back into one of the most critical areas of your life: your health. I want to get a little "sciencey" on you for a minute. So, bear with me. In the end, you'll see we are being watched over by a loving father who truly wants us to be healthy and to succeed in all areas of our lives.

Blaming genetics for your current health state is like blaming your credit card for your debt. Sure, it can play a role in what's happening currently in your state of health, but it doesn't tell the whole story. It plays a tiny part, and that is excellent news! Well, if you're really into putting blame on others, it may not be such great news. But here's why it's such great news! It means that we no longer are set in our health outcomes. Your family history is just that, history! I told you God loves you, and when He sent His son to save us, He also transformed our ability not to be struck down by the so-called sins of our fathers! It's great news! So, what does this all mean? First, you can only point fingers at one person for your health, you. You did it. Not your mom or grandma. Not your dad or your great uncle twice removed on your dad's side. It's you. The sooner you can come to grips with this, the faster you can begin moving forward to reach your true God-given potential.

The truth is, YOU have complete control over your health, which is good news. Remember who your creator is; He doesn't make junk! He doesn't make mistakes, and He didn't start making them on you or your family. Genetics plays a role but a small one. It doesn't define the whole story. Sure, we can have genes that can cause cancer or be more likely to have a specific ailment. If you live a lifestyle that allows those genes to be expressed, then you're more likely to develop that disease. We can allow ourselves to behave in a way that raises our chances of developing a disease, and then we are quick to blame our genetics. Remember this fact: GOD DOES NOT MAKE JUNK! God made you; therefore, you ARE NOT JUNK!

So, how does this all play out in life? It all has to do with epigenetics. I'll keep this simple. Breaking the word apart, epi means above or upon. So, the word means "above the genes." We have historically thought that our genes will dictate our health and the outcomes of our health. Mom or dad had cancer, and my genetics say then I will get cancer. We see so often now women with a gene that may cause breast cancer preemptively have mastectomies to PREVENT the disease! This infuriates me! We have again been lied to about how our bodies work. Most of these cases are not even positive for cancer. So, the good news for you and your family is that genes aren't the only thing that produces an effect on your health. Epigenetics has shown that WHAT YOU do and HOW YOU live affects your genetic outcomes! This is excellent news! Why? For one, you have to stop blaming your current situation of health on your ancestors. And two, you have more control over how your genes are expressed than you think by your lifestyle. I told you, you were made in an image of perfection and to live a long and abundant life! Not to just get sick and die early.

Let me speak to those who are currently experiencing a difficult diagnosis. Maybe you're in the middle of a storm or heading into the next one. Be strong; God has you. Remember, you have been created to be healthy; that's what your body desires! Regardless of your choices of how you treat your diagnosis, know that you were created in God's image and are more than able to heal.

You may be facing a health crisis now. Maybe your spouse, child, or close relative is dealing with a health crisis. Understanding this becomes even more important to grasp hold of; what you do now will affect the future health of your family. What your children are doing now will affect their health in the future. Getting healthy now will have a direct influence on your future generations. Epigenetics shows that if you have a gene for obesity and if you were to alter your lifestyle to promote health, then that gene for obesity will be shut OFF. That gene will not be expressed; therefore, you won't be obese, or your offspring won't be overweight due to that gene. If you have a cancer gene and you change your lifestyle to build health, then that cancer gene will be shut off and not cause cancer. So, it matters what you're doing today to shut off your genetics that cause disease. Why is this good news? You are not destined to have your ancestors dictate your future. You have massive input on how you express your health. Be careful; on the other hand, if you live a life that is conducive to turning those genes ON, then yes, your genetics can negatively influence your health and cause disease to develop.

To gain access to God's real healthcare, we need to be living according to His laws. There is a kind of a big BUT though. Remember when I said Jesus is not of this world, well, He's not. Remember when Adam and Eve ate the forbidden fruit? Well, we were given a fantastic gift; it's called free will.

I will often consult with someone about their health and hope to guide them in a direction that I know will help them. Very rarely will we be on different pages while talking. We lay out a plan, and we are all in agreement that this will WORK to get them moving in the direction they want for their life and their health. BUT. Here it comes. The excuses begin to pour in even before they leave the office. "Well, this weekend I have a birthday party, and the following week I'm away for business," "I tried doing this before and I just never followed through." "When we went through all of this before, I stuck with it for a month and did so great! Then I stopped and went back to doing everything I was doing before." There will always be excuses in this life as to why we aren't getting the results we want or think we deserve. There's no difference when it comes to our health. The great gift of free will means we don't have to do anything, we can do whatever we want; but, of course, there are and will be consequences. Some consequences we welcome but others we choose to ignore that they are happening or will ever happen.

In those above conversations, when someone who truly wants to do the right things and they need to have a long-term change in their life, I know that they mean it. The issues become not about how to do something but why they want to do it. As Nietzsche wrote, "He who has a Why to live for can bear almost any How." See, the excuses begin to pour in when we start getting in the way of what God wants us to do. It happens all the time. The Holy Spirit can be filling us with greatness, and we, in our human minds, can outthink the action or direction He wants us to go in. We're telling ourselves LIES! God will always have our best interests in play, but if we continue to get in the way of where He wants us to go, the pain of getting there will become greater and greater but also more and more difficult.

The barriers to health are often right in front of us, keeping us shackled to a system that does not build health. Even if we try to do the right things, everything around us is fighting for us to fail. So, when the pain doesn't go away instantly and no miracle has happened, we turn to the almighty prescription. We allow our behavior and our history to take control of the things God is trying to correct and to alter our lives for what He has planned for us. We continue on the path of destruction. At the same time, symptoms are hidden away by more prescriptions or over-the-counter medications, and we become further away from our potential.

Even when we are under the care of a healthcare practitioner, it often becomes even more challenging to get healthier. When the doctor speaks, it is as if God himself has spoken to us. We will unquestioningly take any medication in any amount for however long and even do surgeries and whatever else that has nothing to do with getting us healthier. Also, when we ask our doctor if we should exercise or eat better, more often than not, their answer is, "It doesn't matter." On the other hand, when I give someone sensible advice on how to truly change their life and get healthier the way God intended, I get looked at like I have three heads. Something just doesn't add up. We will more likely default to the "easier" route in most things in life, the least painful, but those easier routes in terms of your health will most likely lead to further destruction of your health in the long run.

My goal is for people to reach as close to their God-given potential as possible. That begins with changing how they view themselves and how they approach their healthcare. With all the information out there at our fingertips, we can easily get lost in what we should be doing. Health is a popular topic that makes a ton of money. We're always looking for the next best thing, the next miracle diet, the next supplement or shake that will drop 30 pounds and still be able to eat cake and ice cream. Our wants far exceed what we are willing to do. Do you want massive health? Do you want to be on zero medications? Do you want to grow old, living a high quality of life? I hope you all answered, "Yes!" But who is willing to do what it takes to get there? I'll give you some good news. It's not as hard as you think. Will it take work and consistency? Definitely. Will there be some bumps along the way? Of course. Will there be some pain? I'd be lying if I told you there wouldn't be some, maybe physical, definitely emotional. Will it all be worth it? Without a doubt. Why? God wants all those things for you. He put you here to have an incredible life. But if you don't have your health, there isn't much you can do to fulfill His purpose in your life.

In John 10:10, Jesus says, "The thief comes only to steal and kill and destroy. I came that they may have and enjoy life, and have it in abundance."

We know this verse. I base a lot of my life on it, especially my health. Jesus himself says that there is an enemy out there trying to kill and destroy you and take you off course as quickly as possible and as often as possible. But Jesus saves. He came to give us life and life that we enjoy and have in abundance! Without our health, how difficult it is to achieve God's purpose for us.

1 Corinthians 10:13, "The temptations in your life are no different from what others experience. And God is faithful. He will not allow the temptation to be more than you can stand. When you are tempted, He will show you a way out so that you can endure."

I hope this verse gives you hope. But not an excuse. We all deal with reasons not to do something, especially when it's good for us. The reality of this world is that everything will try to bring you down, especially when you are intentional about doing something to improve what God has given you. When doing what is necessary to achieve health, there will be battles which we will lose and those we will win. When we fail, this is when we press into God more, and in our journey of health, we gain a stronger relationship with Him while He helps lead us to our goal.

Proverbs 16:9, "In their hearts, humans plan their course, but the Lord establishes their steps."

SUMMARY-TAKE 5

- Do not take ownership of your disease.
- Do not allow this world to dictate your future.
- Quit believing the lies about your health.
- You control your health!
- Jesus came to give you life and life with abundance!

CHAPTER 3

YOUR WORTH

Before I formed you in the womb, I knew you,
before you were born, I set you apart;
I appointed you prophets of nations.

Jeremiah 1:5

I was on a weekend getaway with my wife and son at a popular amusement park. We planned one last chance at summer, and we were all looking forward to it before school started again. We stayed at a hotel that was part of the park, so we were shuttled back and forth from our hotel and the park. Of course, everywhere we go, we see the hurt people are in and the struggles they face. If you don't think people are sicker than before and more overweight than ever, just visit your local amusement park and look around. So many people are not living their true God-given potential, not even close. But what I wanted to bring up was a conversation I overheard by a small group of people sitting next to me and behind me. I was right in the middle of the conversation. Now, everyone was excited to go to the park and have their family fun day started, and this group around me was no different. They were in town for a wedding and were visiting the park because it's right nearby and they had many hours before the wedding. Two women were sitting next to each other, along with their spouses, all in their early to mid-forties. They all seemed to be having a great morning and seemed to be happy to be experiencing the park. All four of them were overweight.

Now, don't get me wrong; there's nothing "wrong" with being overweight; I am not judging them. But let me get into their conversation. The couples started talking about the wedding and the clothes they were wearing. The conversation switched over to quite jovial when they began discussing the sizes of their dresses. I hear these types of conversations all the time. We get to the point where how unfit and unhealthy we've become is OK and even comical. Yes, it's harder to stay fit and healthy as people get older. I know some women have had several kids. Let me continue their conversation. They were joking that the only single-digit size piece of clothing they had was their shoe size! I couldn't help but laugh a little, it was funny, they were laughing. My personal favorite was when the woman said that she was so proud of herself for fitting in the same pair of earrings she wore in high school.

I'm not here to judge anyone. We've all been through some difficult times, some more than others, and some incidents we can't even begin to understand. It doesn't change the fact that God wants the very best for us, always. He has way more in store for you than you can even imagine. The previous story was to point out that, over time, we start to feel a little beat down and a little less optimistic that we can ever get back to that normal weight or get healthy enough to stop taking that medication. Throughout our lives, we slowly start to become a shell of who we used to be and lose the fight for God's greatness in our lives. I can only speculate, but if I would have asked those women, "If you could, would you want to lose weight and get in better shape?" They both would have answered like any of us, "Of course." This is how the world works. It slowly takes our spirit of God away from us. The simplest way that the enemy can attack us is by using our health against us. The moment we become sick or hurt, we slowly start the descent away from where God needs us to be.

I hope you begin to see how your health is a significant factor in taking you away from who God called you to be. Without your health, it's nearly impossible to be who God needs you to be. We slowly are pulled away with a barely noticeable sickness or disease. Enough is enough! Your worth and value are beyond measurable; you deserve to be healthy.

How often will you hear someone say that being healthy or doing healthy things just isn't their thing? This gets me so fired up, especially if they're a Christian! The odds of becoming you are roughly 1 in 102,685,000, or 10 followed by 2,685,000 zeros. For comparison, the universe only has 10^{80} atoms. Basically, your odds of living to become you is zero. So, to have such a cavalier attitude toward our health isn't an option. God chose YOU! It's time to see your worth and why God needs you to be your best.

In Jeremiah 1:5, God says, "Before I formed you in the womb I knew you before you were born, I set you apart; I appointed you prophets of nations."

There's a lot in this verse. Sometimes, when I read through the Bible, I can easily get caught up in the antiquity of the Bible and forget that God is speaking to us. This can quickly happen in this verse, but it's crucial when we read the Bible to stay focused on what it's saying to us. We know that becoming a particular human being is practically zero, and you have much better odds of winning the lottery multiple times than becoming that person. So, when God speaks here, it is absolutely reassuring that God not only wants us here, He needs us here. He says that BEFORE we were present in our mother's womb, before she became pregnant, God knew us! He knew He wanted us to become His children. Before we were born, we were set apart.

Being set apart is crucial. You were not placed on this Earth and given the gift of life to be one amongst everyone else. You have been called to be set apart from everyone else with your gifts and talents that God gave you. Not to fit in or just get by and float through this life. Your life has meaning and purpose. I hope we can all agree on this. Now, what that purpose is, I don't know, but I guarantee that to truly fulfill your purpose and to be who God has called you to be, you must have your health. It's difficult to be a Christ-follower when you're sick, suffering, or dead. I believe that Christians should be the healthiest, fittest people on the planet. We've got quite a battle formed against us; we need to be healthy.

We need to be able to understand our worth in the eyes of Jesus. This world is a dark place, and we can quickly lose sight of who we are and whose we are. When the women were talking playfully on the bus, there seemed to be a loss of who they were. It doesn't make them wrong or bad; it just looks as if their circumstances in this world have taken them over. I believe that our overall healthcare has done just that to us. We are given little to no information on what's actually causing our problems and given more and more prescriptions to try to see if that may get us better. It's an endless cycle. So, what does the Bible say, what does God say about this?

In Romans 12:2, Paul says, "Do not be conformed to this world, but be transformed by the renewal of your mind, that by testing you may discern what the will of God is, what is good and acceptable and perfect."

Paul makes an important point in this verse and in understanding that when it comes to our health, we must begin to do things that the world has not led us to do. We must transform our mentality away from treating a disease (human disease care) and, instead, to building and promoting health the way God intended (God's healthcare). Let me be clear; this is by far one of the most critical aspects of our health we need to alter, how we think about and view our health. If not, we end up like everyone else, which is not a good place. My prayer for all of you is to understand how amazing you are. No matter your situation, diagnosis, genetic abnormality, you are created to be an overcomer. It's just that simple. When Jesus talks about being born again in Him, the old you has died and He now lives in you. And guess what? He has overcome this world. I think you're meant for more than your current situation. Even if you're on top of the world, I believe God continues to use you and grow you for more.

In Genesis 1:27, it states that God created us in HIS image. If He is perfect and has no flaws, when did we begin to think that we aren't worthy of health or anything else significant for that matter? Yes, we are inherently flawed, but we still possess God's greatness. When it comes to our health, it's no different. We are worthy of abundant health. Remember John 10:10; He came to give us life to the fullest, in abundance. I feel we have forgotten all about this. Yes, Jesus came to this Earth to save our eternal souls, but why have we allowed our broken world to take away some of the most valuable assets we have, health being one of them. Did God only send His son to die for us so that we can only have eternal life? If so, why not just end this world now? There is so much more for us on this Earth that God would love to see us do and, more importantly, do in His name, to glorify Him!

Remember. Jesus came to die for you, so that you may have eternal life (John 3:16), but life with abundance (John 10:10). There is true love in what Jesus did for you, for all of us. I won't get preachy here, but I think it's essential to drive this point of your worth and the value of your life home. John 3:16 says, "God so loved the world, He sent His only son (to die for us) so that we may have eternal life and not perish." In all His glory, Jesus needed to be made flesh, to be put on this Earth as we are. He was tempted by the things we are tempted by. He lived among those who want Him to fail, be sick, be knocked off His purpose, never find His purpose, and die having lived a meaningless life. If you read through the Gospels, you'll see the story of Jesus' death. It was brutal, something no human should ever have to endure. But Jesus did it. He did it for you. He knew His life on this Earth was for one reason, to die that we may be saved. If you know Jesus, you'll have life everlasting; but we don't want to enter that everlasting life prematurely by living a destructive lifestyle that leads to sickness and death. He was brutally beaten and hung on a cross to give us life and life to the fullest. I think we should live the best we possibly can to honor His sacrifice and love for us. Romans 5:8 says, "But God shows his love for us in that while we were still sinners, Christ died for us."

Can you even begin to imagine loving something or someone enough to know that your life was going to end in a brutal murder to save them? I can't even fathom the thought. I would be so far gone, it wouldn't be funny. So, I'm thankful. I'm grateful that Jesus died for us, that He paid the price for our sinful world because He loved us. I believe that we can love Him and show Him we love Him by honoring His love for our lives by honoring our bodies and living more for Him than for ourselves.

See, when Jesus came to die for us, God knew what He was doing. He knew He had to send a savior to bail us out of our world, His SON! He knowingly turned His back on His only child, to watch Him die, to save us. That should give you goosebumps. Imagine that. God only turned His back on humanity once, so that it would never have to be done again.

As a father, it almost makes me sick when I think of the action God took upon His child, and place it on an Earthly level. If you have children, you'll understand what I mean. If you don't, let me explain. Before I had my son, I never really understood the love a parent has for their child. Now, it makes sense why parents are the way they are toward their kids, always checking in on them, making sure they're OK. Did they have enough to eat for breakfast? How was their day at school? Parents have so many questions, but only because of a love that has no equal.

My son was born in April of 2016. You may have gathered that I am not the biggest fan of medical care. So, we opted to have as little intervention as possible when Jack was being born. Everything was going according to plan; my wife was progressing as well as we could have asked. His heart rate was good; my wife was laboring like a champ. No pain medication, no induction, just doing what God intended her body to do. Late into labor, after hours of pushing, Jack's heart rate began to drop during contractions and while my wife was pushing. This was not good. We couldn't have a baby in a healthy way if during contractions and pushing his heart rate would drop significantly. By that, I mean a reasonable heart rate of 140 dropped down to the low 80's. We had no idea what was happening to him. As we got to the hospital room to have her further evaluated, the doctor on staff said everything was OK, and my wife could continue laboring if she wanted to, and after some time, they could use forceps to pull Jack out. That wasn't an option. My wife battled for hours and hours. It truly is a testament to the strength of what God did to make woman. I know I couldn't do it! But after considering all possibilities, we decided to have him via a C-section. This went against all our plans. We thought God just didn't show up. What happened? After all this time and months of preparation, we end up like this. It was more than difficult, to say the least, especially on my wife. But we knew God had bigger plans for us. And sometimes we do everything right and the outcome we expect just doesn't happen. But we lean on God even more in those times, and we continue to do the best we can and purse God in all areas.

After Jack was born, nearly all ten pounds of him, the nurses checked him out. I kissed my wife and ran to be with my son. His oxygen level was low, about 80%, and the average value for blood oxygen is in the upper 90's. Jack was brought to the nursery to be monitored, and our midwife and I followed closely behind. At this point, I felt this was the last place I wanted to be, but it was the only place I needed to be. Lauren was heading to recovery and had no idea what was happening with the child she had carried for 41 weeks.

In the nursery, the nurses advised me to leave Jack in his "bassinet." I use that term loosely; it's more of a box they put your baby into while they check on them. As I see him lying there, crying, his oxygen levels low, and just born. He was alone. As a father for all of eight minutes, something kicked in. I didn't care what the nurses said. I didn't care what tests they needed to run. All that mattered was making sure Jack knew I was there and he was going to be alright. So, without much thought, I snatched Jack out of his bassinet and just held him. I spoke to him as I knew he would know my voice from the months of talking to him through his momma's belly. In that instant, a literal moment, upon picking him up, he immediately stopped crying, and we watched as his oxygen levels began to rise to normal. The nurse on duty came scurrying over to make me put him down, and a little bit of poppa bear came out as I said, "He's fine! His levels are getting to normal; he's fine!" She thought the best thing for Jack was to be left alone, in a strange place, with all these lights on him, screaming! Going from a safe and protected womb of a loving mother to being alone, poked and prodded, and screaming. This is what that nurse thought would be best for my son. "Crying is good for him," she said. "It'll help get more oxygen in him." I'm not sure about this logic. If anyone is hysterical, crying and screaming, they don't get more oxygen; they get less. They feel as if they're hyperventilating. In my arms is where Jack stayed. Soon after getting there, I just left the nursery with Jack to get him to his mom, so he could finally eat.

Let me bring this back to God's faithful love for us and to show how truly worthy you are. Ever since Jack was born, he's been my best buddy. I love him. But you see, I would do anything to never have him experience pain, injury, heartbreak, loss, or anything that would inflict negativity on him. But that's just not the world we live in. It's a part of this world. All I can do is try to protect as best I can and limit his pain to something that will make him grow and get stronger. If you are a parent, you know what I mean. It hurts your soul when you see your child get hurt or observe an act of hate put on them. Jack has experienced a few sicknesses over his life, but each time, when he would be snotty, throw up, or have a fever, as a parent, all I wanted was to take it away from him and put it on myself. But I know that's not possible. He needs to work through it and understanding in the end that he'll be healthier and stronger. But I would never have left his side when he's feeling unwell. He won't go through it alone. Now imagine, your child or niece or nephew or grandchild being sick. Would you just leave them in their room alone while you went on with your day? Doubt it! I could only imagine you'd be right there with them. Or worse yet, would you turn your back and allow your young child to play near a busy highway? Can you imagine that feeling? The anxiety and fear that would come upon you if you had to turn away as your child walked right into traffic. It's unbearable just to think about.

God turned His back on His son, just once, so that He would never have to do it again. As a father, I never even want to think about having to do that. God knew what He was doing. As brutal as it sounds, turning His back on His son, to watch Him live a life on Earth that would inevitably end in misery and early death, it was necessary. Jesus came to overcome this world, and He has. Do not think for a second that your life isn't worth living. There was an ultimate sacrifice so that you may have life and, again, have a life with abundance! You are worth more than you can ever imagine. God in heaven never turns His back on you. He wants more for you than you could ever even imagine.

As we move along with our God-centered health journey, we will see that God is always right with us and watching over us. See, when Jack was learning to walk, climb, or cross a street, my wife or I were always right there with him to protect him from serious harm. I tower over a four-year-old, but my hand is almost always extended down toward him, in case he wants to hang onto it. To make him feel safer. I believe this is our God, in all aspects of our life. His hand is always extended to us; it's just up to us to reach up and grab it. The more we grasp onto Him, the safer and more effective our journey through this life will be. It may not cause less harm and pain, but we'll be more protected. The same goes for our health. The more we can anchor to God and the laws He placed upon this Earth, the better we'll be.

Psalm 139:13-14 says, "For you formed my inward parts; you knitted me together in my mother's womb. I praise you, for I am fearfully and wonderfully made. Wonderful are your works; my soul knows it very well."

And 1 Corinthians 6:20 reads, "For you were bought with a price. So glorify God in your body."

We can easily overlook how amazing our human bodies are. We see so much brokenness, faults, disease, and worldly devastation that we forget that God truly knitted us from His design to create a masterpiece that only He could build. Regardless of your current situation or what you may think is bad luck, God has a purpose for you, and He is leading you toward victory.

As a Christian in today's world, it's easy to assume that we have a spirit of cowardness or even weakness. It seems to be uncool to be a Christian in the media's eyes. It can almost be difficult to say you're a Christian in some groups in fear of some social persecution. This kind of mentality relates right back to your personal and spiritual health. God didn't spend all this time forming you, knowing every hair on your head and every freckle on your face, to sit back and give you a spirit of weakness! No way! Being a Christian does not make you weak. It is precisely the opposite. You were given a spirit of strength to stand out and to overcome!

Jesus did not go through this world only to die and then leave you with a lame spirit. Are you kidding me? If this is how you're feeling about your life and your health, you need to stop and remember who created you. Even if your mom or dad left you when you were little or no one has ever said that they love you and you feel alone in this world, God loves you. If you're sick or overweight or have a physical handicap, you have a spirit of God that is an overcomer. You are strong. He has overcome this physical world already. All your sicknesses, diagnoses, and physical ailments are over. Now is the time to realize this and show God that you love Him by living according to His laws that govern your life and health.

No matter your current state of health, we will work together to gain ground on becoming healthier. For I truly believe, and I hope you do too, that being healthy is what God needs for us. Especially in a world full of sickness, disease, and God's children being pulled further from their purpose. You, as a Christ-follower, need your health. Your family needs your health. This world needs your health. If getting healthy has been on your heart for some time now and getting there was always a little confusing or indirect, now is the time you make a move. Show this world your love of God by being who God called you to be.

SUMMARY-TAKE 5

- God sent His son to die for you so that you may have LIFE!
- You are not here by accident; God planned you well before you were born!
- You have massive value, and your health is crucial to pursue your purpose
- You are not weak; you have a spirit of God, of victory!
- Your health is necessary, honor God by honoring your body.

CHAPTER 4

WHAT IS HEALTH?

You are of God, little children, and have overcome
them because He who is in you is greater than
he who is in the world.

1 John 4:4.

In this chapter, you will begin to see the power of your body. It is crucial to understand what health is, and maybe just as importantly, what health is not. I've noticed that most people do not have a grasp on health. We get too caught up in our daily lives, almost in a survival mode, that we ignore our health. When we realize that something is amiss, we may ignore it for a while then go to the doctor for a quick fix, a medication most likely, and this is how we manage most of our health. We wake up, go to work, be with family, go on vacations, do things around the house, and just go about our daily lives. When we have a symptom that impairs our daily activities, we stop everything and try to fix it as quickly as possible with medication. While that symptom may go away, we never really get to the cause of what happened. We do not honor our bodies. Now, there's nothing inherently wrong with this; however, if all we ever do is wait to have a symptom to begin "fixing" it, we are just waiting for a massive health crisis to occur. Whether or not we realize it, this is what we've been doing our entire lives.

Almost daily, I get asked this question or a version of it: "What can I do about my symptom?" Fill in the blank with whatever your symptoms may be at the time. Perhaps you suffer from headaches, neck pain, digestive problems, toe fungus, numbness, diabetes, cancer, sciatica, the flu, etc. You name it, people want a solution today, now. Very rarely will they ask the better question, "What is causing my problem?" But this is what we've been doing for our entire lives, is it not? We live worrying about all the other things like money, relationships, kids, and work and never put our own personal health in the forefront until something happens. Then we wonder, *What the heck happened! I was healthy before I got cancer* or *I thought I was super healthy; how did I have a heart attack? I just went to the doctor, and they said everything was normal!* These are the conversations we put in our heads, and when we begin to lose our health in some way, we are quick to look all around for how it happened and never really look at ourselves for developing sickness over our lifetime. We have been led astray to not knowing what being healthy is.

We continue to live a lifestyle without God in the midst of it and are actively being destructive toward our health. Then we wonder what happened when a diagnosis shows up. In this chapter, I will begin to show you that before whatever health crisis or diagnosis you or your close ones are going through or have been through, you were not healthy leading up to that problem. Let me say that again. Before your symptoms or health problem, you were not healthy.

What is Health? Let's begin here. If I asked one hundred people how they define health, or how would they know they are healthy, how would they respond? How would you respond? Well, I've asked those one hundred people, and the majority answered in a very similar fashion. But take a minute and think about it. How would you define health? How would you know if you're truly healthy? There is an actual definition that is 100% clear as to what health is; it also leaves out what health is not. But to answer my question, how would you define health? Some of you most likely will have answered, "feeling good," or "having lots of energy," or "not being sick," or "eating well and exercising." Did I get most of them? Is there anything else? "Not being stressed," "having a great spiritual relationship with Jesus." There are always some more "interesting" definitions I've heard over the years, but these are by far the most common. To be honest, they are not wrong definitions, but none are the definition of health. I would argue that if you are healthy, then the above descriptions are what happens when you're healthy.

Before I tell you what health is, allow me to ask you another question. How important is your health? How important is your child's health? I can only assume you answered in a version of the following: "it's so important, my health is everything! My child's health means so much more than my health!" We all know that health is essential. One of the ways I know you know that it's important is because when we lose our health, it's the one thing we pray for, and the one thing we seek out. It seems to be where all our focus goes. Think about that even if you had a simple cold for four or five or seven days. It's terrible! You have the constant sniffling and blowing your nose, the dry cough, the mucousy cough, maybe a slight fever: all the weird, gross things that come with being sick. You're absent from work for a day or two. And that's just with a cold. What about a stomach virus? Way worse! How about a bad headache, a migraine? What about a more chronic condition that has developed throughout your life as in cancer, diabetes, or heart disease? Health is something we long for and desire, but we only really focus on it when we lose our health. Otherwise, we assume we're doing just fine.

When you answer the question about how important is your health is, the answer should be, "It's the most important asset I have." It's more important than your time, money, job, or even your family. I would argue it may also be above where you put how important God is to you. The reason I say this is because we can be Bible readers, churchgoers, God worshippers, great workers, amazing family men and women, but the second we are sick or diagnosed with something, where does our focus go? It is not on finishing that report for work or putting on the worship music; it is redirected to the sickness Our focus is away from hanging out with our child and onto getting better. I'm not saying that those things are not important; it's just that our health should be the biggest asset in our lives.

As a Christian, let me clarify what I mean by putting God "below" your health. I believe we unintentionally rank things on importance, depending on where we are in our lives. Family, Faith, Work, Health, etc., which is not a bad thing. But when we quickly say that God is the most important thing, or your faith is the most important thing in your life, I almost have to call you out! It is essential, but I think we rank things incorrectly. Having importance means that there is a hierarchy of what you would do before something else. I may claim that God is #1 to me and my family is #2, but if my wife or child were sick or hurt, I would leave whatever I'm doing and go to them, even if I were at church. "Sorry, God, there's something more important than you right now; it's making sure my family is safe." Now, I'll be praying the whole way, but I hope you understand what I'm getting at. Ranking things on importance becomes neglectful when something else happens.

There is a much more useful and practical way of finding importance, and it is not putting God, your family, or even your health at #1, #2, and #3. It does mean putting God in the middle of all those things.

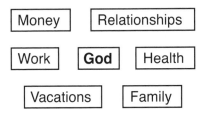

When God then sits in the middle of all the other things we find precious and essential, we begin to make decisions on how God wants us to be and who He wants us to be. When God is in the middle, and we are acting according to His desires for us, we begin to make better decisions and have better outcomes and a more fulfilled life.

Can we all agree then, that your health is among the most critical things in your life and is your biggest asset? With that, I know we can all agree, good health is something God desires for us, and what God needs from us to fulfill His purpose in our lives. Without good health, we move away from who

God called us to be. However, as important as our health is, we have no idea what it is! With so much information in the world, there isn't a whole lot of substance. Hosea 4:6 says, "My people will perish for lack of knowledge." We are missing the truth! We cannot discern what is real and what is fake. This is the reason we put God in the middle of our health and live according to how He made us. Here is what health is, and you can look it up for yourself.

The World Health Organization (WHO) defines health to be this: "a state of complete physical, mental, and social well-being, not merely the absence of disease or infirmity."

The WHO gives us a solid definition for many reasons, but we will add to it later. It makes it clear that we have been thinking about health all wrong for most of our lives. How often do we think about something and make it a truth, and when knowledge enters the equation, we must quickly alter our understanding? See, the world we live in makes us believe that health is feeling good and not being sick. But, in reality, those have very little to nothing to do with what health is. I will even argue that being "sick" or having symptoms does not make you sick or does not imply that you are sick. Hang in there. This is going to be an exciting chapter for most of us. But in the end, you will have a better understanding of how your body works and begin to put more faith in how God created you than what you have previously thought. Remember, God created you in His perfect image; you are not junk. He did not mess you up. He did not forget about you. All we need to start doing is honoring our bodies and stop harming them.

In Jeremiah 29:11, the Lord says, "For I know the plans I have for you, plans for welfare and not for evil, to give you a future and a hope." When we begin to grasp and anchor to God's word, even in our health, watch what you are capable of through God.

Let's get back to the definition of health: "a state of complete physical, mental, and social well-being, not merely the absence of disease or infirmity." To be healthy, yes, this makes sense. It should be clear and concise. Health is not this unicorn we've all been chasing. Health is what God has given to us; health is our body's default. You desire to be healthy. We need to be healthy. However, in the world and society we live in, how to get healthy seems to have us all in disagreement. Health is not doing just one thing or another. We view our health from a feeling perspective or how someone looks or take care of themselves. And we are then conditioned to perceive our health from a perspective of feeling or looking a certain way; then, we decide we are healthy. With all the pharmaceutical commercials and all the drug aisles in the grocery store, we are continually being bombarded with something we can take to feel better or just curb a symptom for a little while longer. I just feel better. Give me instant gratification. This mentality has brought us to a dangerous situation with our health.

Suppose I asked you, "Would taking a medication make you healthy?" How would you respond? Most people I ask nowadays will answer, "No, it just covers up or masks the problem." That's right. Medication at its core does not aim to cure anything but just remove a symptom for as long as possible. Don't get me wrong, some medication is necessary to keep us alive and give us a chance to be healthy, but it does not make us healthy. Again, the removal of a symptom via a medication does not make us healthy.

I am sure that most of you, at some point in your life, have taken medication. Maybe you have had a back pain or headache, high blood pressure, or diabetes. What happens if you were to stop taking your blood pressure medication? Your blood pressure would shoot back up. Start taking it again, and it lowers it. People need this medication. Having high blood pressure for an extended period is dangerous; it's deadly. But the point is, the blood pressure medication is not curing your hypertension. If it did, then you would not have to take it forever. Or any drug for that matter. If a medication aimed to cure something, you would not need it for more than a few days or weeks. We know this isn't the case. Even with something as common as a headache or migraine, people need medication to get through the day to function. But if they were to stop taking their drug, the problem would come back. I hope we can all agree that medications, prescription or over the counter, are not curing us; they are merely masking the symptoms while the body tries to heal.

Health is more than just looking and feeling a certain way. So, we know that just feeling better by taking medication, although good for now, does not make us healthier. The more drugs we take over the course of our lives, the less healthy we become. It is impossible to take medication and get healthy. If one aspirin is said to be safe, what happens if you swallow an entire bottle of aspirin? You die. So, it is toxic. It is dangerous, even in the smallest amounts. The same goes for any other medication. It must be made clear that if someone is on multiple prescriptions at a given time, the further they are from real health and the further they get from God's purpose for their lives.

What about someone who looks a certain way? They have little to no body fat. You can see their ab muscles. They work out, must be eating well, are active, and don't take any medication. They're healthy, right? Is it possible to look fit, have the body we may only dream of, yet drop dead of a heart attack or get diagnosed with cancer? One hundred percent, it is possible. We have all seen people that fit the picture of health have their lives ended much too soon.

On the other hand, I've even seen people who are overweight, never work out, eat terribly, and live well into their 80s or 90s. They may not be living a full and abundant life, but they're alive nonetheless. So, what's the difference? Are some people just lucky? Can you strictly blame it on their genetics? Is health something we are either blessed or cursed with? Does it even matter what we do?

Along with the WHO definition of health, we need to add something significant. Even though their definition covers most of the basis of health, it dances around a vital aspect of health. To define health, we must add in this,

Health is how well our bodies are HEALing. Health is about 100% functioning.

Think about this. If you recall from earlier, God has created our bodies in His perfect image. Nothing, no thing is left out or extra; all things serve a purpose. We are meant and designed to be healthy. John 10:10 says that Jesus came so that we may have an abundance. Health is all about abundance, maximizing our potential. It has nothing to do with being cursed in our genetics or just bad luck. It comes down to how well your body is functioning and healing.

Along with our fundamental understanding of health—optimal physical, mental, and social well-being and not just the absence of disease—good health occurs when our bodies are functioning and healing at their God-given potential and as close to 100% as possible.

If your body were healing correctly, how could you develop cancer? Could your heart just stop working? Would you catch a cold or the flu? Now, this is where the rubber meets the road. You need to begin to honor your body and work to improve your health or how your body is healing and functioning to remove these types of symptoms. Just look at the word "HEALTH." Two-thirds of the word is "HEAL." If you are healing, you are healthy. If your body is not healing, you cannot be healthy, and no amount of medication will improve your health. It will only mask and manage the symptom.

What about symptoms?

Symptoms are the body's way of telling you, "Something ain't right." Just as a "low fuel" icon lights and starts beeping in your car or a "check engine" icon shows up, that is just the symptom of something else occurring. If we were to manage our vehicles like we manage our health, we could just put a piece of black tape over the check engine light or low fuel light. Is that not what we do with our health? Just make it go away or ignore it, and maybe it will disappear. Cover it up and deal with it later. If you neglect your low fuel light long enough, what happens?

Even if you are sincere in prayer about it, "God give me more fuel!" The laws of the world will quickly catch up to you, and you'll be stuck, having to deal with a much more complicated situation. One that could have been avoided if you just honored that symptom and put some gas in your car, even a dollar's worth, to get you home. The thing with our health is that when symptoms show up, usually there has been a problem for quite some time, potentially years. So, if we continue to ignore or mask symptoms, we will be dealing with a significant health crisis. A lot of us take better care of our cars than we do our bodies! Imagine that! From two tiny cells over 10 months, we get a living, breathing, growing being. Yet we put more time and effort into making sure our cars are in good shape than taking care of our health. It is mind-boggling. We are creatures of hypocrisy. We know how important our health is, yet we rarely do anything to improve our health. We would rather spend more time and money ignoring our bodies, brush whatever it is under the rug, and just "deal with it later." You cannot afford to wait to get healthier. Recall the statistics from the beginning, cancer, heart disease, obesity, chronic illness? These are happening to you and your loved ones! Not in five years or twenty, but NOW! Conditions are developing now, so NOW is the best time to begin improving your health and healing. Begin to function at a higher level.

I'll let you in on a little secret about your body's amazing ability to function and heal. But it comes as a double-edged sword. Unlike your car, your body can and does adapt to its environment constantly. It is ALWAYS trying to help you and keep you alive. It NEVER tries to harm you; it will not do the wrong thing. It will perform at the highest possible level for as long as it can. BUT, and it's a pretty big but, if we continue to create an environment of sickness and disease, your body can only adapt for so long until, eventually, it must give in. There is a limitation of what it can tolerate. As we know, it takes a lot for our bodies to show up with a symptom or disease, this is why we must act now to improve our health and not when we have a diagnosable problem.

So, symptoms, like the check engine light, show up when something has not been functioning right. Sometimes, we don't even realize symptoms are there until they become an issue. If you think about it, symptoms are a good thing! This may sound like a wild and crazy thought but think about it. If you sprained your ankle, what happens? It explodes with swelling, fluid, and PAIN: all symptoms of a sprained ankle. These symptoms force you NOT to put pressure on your foot. So, if you just take some painkillers and it completely blocks the pain, you may be able to walk on your hurt ankle. But what happens then? It gets worse! If we continue that cycle, your ankle will never heal properly, and you'll be dealing with a much bigger issue down the road. Make sense? Pain and swelling are good; they're supposed to happen. Your body is doing what it is made to do. If you honored your symptoms of a sprained ankle, what would you do? Rest it. Maybe put some ice on it for the pain. Stay off it. Maybe do some therapy after a few days to build strength and movement. Honor your symptoms; do not ignore them. Do not cover them up.

What about fevers? I often ask my patients if having a temperature is a good thing or a bad thing? We have been conditioned to answer quickly to this one. Typically, the response is, "A bad thing." I think we respond so quickly to this particular question because it is a symptom of the body that we do not enjoy. It's no fun to have a fever. It's not fun to experience your child having a fever. I've been there—multiple times. For us to be healthy, we need to begin to understand our bodies and begin to honor them; after all, God did create us. Nothing that our bodies do is trying to harm us. The best thing we can do when a symptom pops up is to ask, "Why is my body doing this? What is the purpose of it?" If you know that your body is doing everything it can to help you and save you and that God created you from two cells to what you are, then you begin to see things differently. Let me ask you, "Is a fever a good thing or a bad thing?" Before you answer, think about it. Take the feeling out of it. Forget about how uncomfortable it can be. Good or bad? I hope you answered, "Fever is a good thing."

But why is having a fever a good thing? Doesn't that mean you're sick? I like to answer that kind of question a little differently. It's not that you're sick; your body is just expressing symptoms, doing what it's designed to do. If you have a run-in with a specific bacteria that your body is unable to deal with, and that bacteria is now trying to harm you, guess what your body will do? Spike a fever! Why? Bacteria cannot survive above a specific temperature. Your brilliant body is fixing the problem without you even thinking about it. If we lower the fever artificially, we slowly weaken our bodies. It's not fighting anymore; it just gets weaker so we can feel better now. Our immune system then doesn't get stronger, and we become more susceptible to infection. With the use of antibiotics, the more we take, the weaker our immune system becomes, and the cycle continues. Honor your symptoms.

What about a virus? A fever induced by a virus can run a little higher than that of bacterial infection. Why? Viruses can be more durable; they need more heat to kill them off. Again, your body is doing what it is supposed to do. If you let your body do what it is supposed to do, the fever will never get out of control; it won't cause seizures. However, this is why less intervention is best. Temperatures that go beyond 105 or 106 degrees, that last more than a few hours are typically caused by outside interference or intervention that disallows the body to regulate the temperature on its own.

Cancer is a symptom that may be more difficult to wrap our heads around, but it is a symptom nonetheless. This symptom can become extremely dangerous and deadly. So how can we honor our bodies when cancer shows up? I get it. I've lost family and friends to cancer. I'll repeat myself; the body is always trying to heal itself; it is still trying to do the best possible thing to survive, and never trying to harm us. Cancer is an abnormal cell. If we never make an abnormal cell, we can never get cancer. The truth is, we all make abnormal cells; it's a part of living. Abnormal cells develop because the environment becomes abnormal or unsafe. The fantastic thing about our bodies is that every cell in our body will eventually die, and a new cell will take its place. If your body is healing, every few years, you will have a brand-new body with new organs, new eyes, new skin, new lungs, all new cells. All we need to do is make healthy cells!

However, when the environment we create within our bodies becomes unlivable, instead of just dying, our bodies adapt— without us even knowing it. We will make abnormal cells (cancer) multiple times over our lives and never even know it. We can overcome cancer; we do it every day. So why does it become a problem? Why can it overtake our lives and even cause death? When those abnormal cells are no longer dying, and healthy cells are no longer being produced, you begin to replicate abnormal cells. If we continue this cycle of creating abnormal cells over time, cancer can now be diagnosed by testing. Developing cancer is a process that can take years.

If we create an environment that is one of health, we get health. If we create an environment that is conducive to build disease, we get disease. What environment? The environment in which we live, our body. Are we doing things and living a life that is building health or building sickness? It's one or the other. We are either moving toward health or disease.

The symptoms we face are numerous, far too many to outline, but when something does occur in someone's life, think and ask, "Why is this happening?" Are these boogers flowing out of their nose a good thing or a bad thing? Should I stop it or support their body? The boogers are removing toxins from the body. The diarrhea is moving harmful "stuff" out quickly, sometimes, a little too fast. Vomiting? Get the bad stuff out before my body has to process it. It's doing what it is supposed to do. Broken bone? Swelling happens almost instantly to protect the area. White blood cells and bone repairing cells are on the job right away. The body is doing what it is supposed to do. It will heal.

I have seen many patients throughout my career; they often have the same types of problems. I understand that when someone has a symptom, they let me know about it. That's fine. They are looking for advice on how to get rid of that symptom. I will give them something they can do for their soreness, or numbness, or sickness to help aid the body in healing. But it often comes down to them wanting something to get rid of the problem now! I usually do not say this to my patients, but I have. "Not every symptom is an emergency." We are not used to feeling symptoms. We are not used to having to wait something out for the body to heal. We know it is capable of healing, but we do not have the patience or the mental capability to allow it to do so. No one ever said that being sick or having the flu or expressing some sort of symptom would be easy or fun. But the more we can tolerate these things without needing some sort of chemical intervention, the better we become in the long run, the healthier we become. We have just become so quick to take something and forget that our bodies are trying to tell us something. So instead of giving the body what it may need or stop giving it what it does not need, we run to the medicine cabinet or the doctor's office for a prescription and interfere with what the body is naturally trying to do: heal. It may be time to embrace the suckiness of being "sick."

* * * Disclaimer * * *

If there is a crisis, as in you broke a bone, uncontrolled bleeding, infection spreading, or there is a major accident that your body can't adapt to right away, you need to go to the hospital, now! Our medical system shines in times of crisis. It will save your life. That system, however, is not designed to bring you health.

For everything else that is not an emergency, honor your body, honor the symptoms. Support your body in its ability to heal.

Romans 8:37 says, "Yet in all these things we are more than conquerors through Him who loved us."

It appears throughout the bible that we are God's creation. We can do all things through Christ. We cannot forget that we are conquerors, and this verse says MORE than conquerors. You are not a mistake. Your health does not come by chance. It begins by honoring your body and understanding who created it and that you are more than capable of overcoming any dysfunction or disease. That is who you are! You are a healer, and health is what you deserve.

SUMMARY-TAKE 5

- Health is about optimal functioning and healing, not just the absence of disease.
- Symptoms are your body's way of telling you something is not right.
- Do not ignore symptoms or mask them, honor them!
- Embrace the suck when you do feel unwell. You will only get stronger.
- You are more than a conqueror. You are an overcomer.

CHAPTER 5

THE MASTER CONTROLLER

Do Not skip this chapter. It may be the missing link

I am the vine; you are the branches.
If you remain in me and I in you, you will bear much fruit;
apart from me, you can do nothing.

John 15:5

In our last chapter, we discussed what health is and what it is not. We started to see that our bodies are made to be healthy; they were designed to heal. We also added a crucial aspect of health: 100% functioning, and healing. If our body is functioning on all cylinders, working just the way it is supposed to, we would be healthy. We may begin to ask questions like, "How do I know I'm functioning well?" or "I think I'm healthy; I feel good, right?" Remember that health has little to nothing to do with how we are feeling or how we look. But there is something that does control our bodies and how they function and, in turn, how they heal. So regardless of our current health situation, whether we're living with cancer, diabetes, or no diagnosis at all and we are doing pretty well, we still need to get healthier. I assume this is something we can all agree on?

Our current model of healthcare has failed us in getting well. We think we are healthy because a test comes back negative or there is nothing to diagnose yet. The medical tests we use are only so good to find a problem. Once there is a problem, we never know how to get healthy and correct the cause of the problem. We are given something to take to remove the symptoms, but never truly getting healthy.

So, what controls your health? What controls all functions, ALL the functions of your body? What physically allows you to work, to stay alive?

Think about this: where did God put all the ability of your body to heal and function? You may have said, "My heart." Maybe it is "the immune system." Those are the most common answers before we realize what controls everything. YOUR BRAIN! Think about it. Of course, your brain is the most vital organ. God placed it in bone to surround and protect it. All functions and all healing come from your brain. Here comes the next part. Our bodies have not become a wireless device. It is hardwired. So how does the brain communicate to the rest of your body? How does your brain make your big toe wiggle, your eyes blink, your arms move? How does your heart beat or your lungs breathe? How does your stomach know when to digest food or to know that something is too hot to touch? YOUR NERVOUS SYSTEM is the master controller of your body. It is made up of your brain, spinal cord, and nerves, which connect to all muscles, tissues, cells, and organs.

We cannot disregard this. I know all doctors know this: the brain controls it all. It's in all our medical textbooks, "the nervous system controls and coordinates all functions of the body." So how is your nervous system functioning? I'll give you the most common answers I get: "I think it's working fine," "I'm not nervous," "I'm sure, not well," or "I'm always nervous!" How would you answer that question? If you said something like the above answers, you're like everyone else. We have a general misunderstanding or just plain ignorance about our health and how our bodies work. Yet, we all know what controls our bodies and quickly forget about it and look everywhere else to fix a problem.

You must anchor to this point. Your healing potential comes from your nervous system functioning as well as it can. Imagine if I cut the nerves that connect your brain to your left arm. What would happen to your left arm? Could it move? Nope! It would no longer work, regardless of what you ate for breakfast or what supplements you're taking. What about disconnecting your nerves that run from the brain, down your spinal cord to your heart. If those nerves were disconnected, what happens to your heart? It stops! You die. We can do this for any of the nerves connecting your brain to your body, even your immune system, and endocrine system. All the power and potential come from your brain, down your spinal cord, and out the nerves to every part of your body.

It's easy to understand that if any nerve were disconnected entirely from the body part or organ system it was controlling, that part of the body would no longer work. But what happens when there is pressure, physical pressure on the spinal cord, or the nervous system? I think we can agree that the body part or the organ would not just stop working. But would it work to its full capacity? No, it can't. Think about this as a dimmer switch to a lamp. When the switch is fully on, the lights are working correctly and as bright as they can be. However, when we use the dimmer, what happens to the lights? They get less bright. Our medical system is summed up by this analogy.

When an organ is not working correctly, or there is something wrong with your body, we look to that organ or body part as the problem. If you dimmed the lights to 50%, would you change the light bulbs because they aren't as bright as they should be? Of course not! You would go to the source of the power, turn the switch to fully on. Problem fixed. The light is now working at 100%. The same goes for the function of our bodies. When there is a symptom or diagnosis, we always just look at what's ailing us and never ask, 'What's causing this issue and how can I get my body to function and heal better?

To improve your health and functioning, you have to address your nervous system. After all, it is controlling your body. There's more to this. Like I've said many times already, God created your body perfectly to work in harmony with all of the systems of the body and create an environment of healing. He put our brains in bone (skull) to protect it, but He put the next most crucial part in bone as well. Your spinal cord is surrounded by your spine, to protect the spinal cord.

The great thing about your spine is that it is movable. So, along with providing protection and support of your body, to keep you upright and moving, it allows you to bend, twist, dance, and swing golf clubs. Would anyone disagree that your spine is crucial? I hope not. This is where I get frustrated. Everyone knows that your brain and spinal cord control all the functions of our bodies. We all know that the skull and spine surround and protect those organs. We wear helmets and do our best to protect our head and brain from injury, but we forget to take care of our spines! We are never getting them checked. Never even addressing them. It's mind-boggling to me. See, this has nothing to do with pain, but everything to do with function.

Let's bridge the gap. Your skull and spine protect your brain and spinal cord, the most important system we have in our bodies. This is where God put your incredible healing power. The nervous system is the first system to develop as we are in utero. We know if we disconnected a nerve to an organ or body part, that part would no longer work. What happens if we were to squeeze a nerve or put pressure on it? Well, is there any way possible that nothing happens? If there was pressure on a nerve going to your heart, lungs, thyroid, or fingers, is there any way that everything would still be working at 100%. No! There is never a situation in which a nerve is being blocked or pinched, minimizing its ability to transfer messages from the brain to your body, and everything still works perfectly. Remember the dimmer switch. I think this is an easy concept to understand; however, when it pertains to us as individuals, it becomes an afterthought. Of course, your spine is essential, of course, the structure and health of my spine is vital, but why would we ever think twice to maintain it and keep it working well? If someone has severe scoliosis, is that a good thing or a bad thing? Every five-year old in my office can answer that with authority, "It's bad!" So, what happens when our spines are ten degrees out of position? Five degrees? One degree? Would you want any pressure on the nerves controlling your heart? How much pressure is OK on the nerves traveling from your brain, down your spine, and out to your digestive system? How much pressure is OK on the nerves going to your child's heart or lungs? No amount of pressure on your nervous system is OK. Our only goal is to minimize the interference and damage to our spine, affecting our nervous system.

As the spine is designed to surround and protect our spinal cords, it can also cause damage to the spinal cord if put in the wrong position. Our spine is meant for good, but can lead to interference and decreased function, and, therefore, dis-ease.

In our current healthcare system, I genuinely believe everyone understands the importance of our brain-body connection and how our spinal cord and nerves control and maintain our bodies. God created it to do so. The problem becomes most of us never even know if there is a problem with our spine and nerve system unless something happens or a symptom arises. Even then, our first stop is usually a medical office that will address our symptoms, never the cause. If you have damage in your spine and it's obstructing the normal flow of power from your brain to your bowels, there's no way your bowels are working correctly. There is never a scenario that taking medication builds your health. Remember, your organs, muscles, and your entire body, only do what your brain tells them to do.

I get this question a lot: "If this is so important," and I think we all know that it is, "why doesn't my doctor tell me about this?" Great question! It is a simple answer. It's not what they do. They do not address your spine and nerve system. Their job is to diagnose and treat. When your symptom goes away from the medication they gave you, they did their job. But we have to know that we are not any healthier but further from health.

So, have you had your spine and nervous system checked before? What should your spine even look like? From the front, we all know it needs to be straight. From the side, it needs to have three curves. This structure surrounds and protects your nervous system. In this position, all function is happening optimally. Your spine will not degenerate. It won't allow discs to bulge and herniate. It won't cause damaging effects on your nervous system. So, what does your spine look like? Is it normal or abnormal? Are you building health or sickness?

Remember, your nervous system controls all functions in your body. Health is 100% function. Therefore, if your nervous system is functioning at 100%, you will be healthy. If your nervous system is not functioning at 100%, then you are building sickness or dis-ease. The structure of your spine protects your nerve system, so the structure of your spine is crucial for optimal functioning and for you to be healthy. Structure determines function, and function determines health. Your spine's health = your health.

This entire principle, this whole point is based on how God created your body to operate. This principle describes chiropractic. Everyone I ever have a conversation with about all the above agrees. It all makes sense, until I mention chiropractic. Chiropractors address the nervous system like no one else. They are the ones trained in correcting that "dimmer switch." They are the ones trained in finding and detecting where your spine is hindering your healing potential. If your spine is abnormal, chiropractors can help correct it. Without surgery, without tortuous devices, they find and adjust your spine and, in turn, allow your nervous system to function better. Improved function means improved health.

I've been doing this long enough to have heard all the responses from, "I'm Dr. Dan, I'm a chiropractor." I have heard all the negatives of being a chiropractor and what people think of chiropractic. Everyone is entitled to their opinion. However, it doesn't mean there is truth behind it. There is a principle, a law to how our bodies work. It isn't my definition; it's God's! Chiropractic is all about increasing your body's ability to heal by addressing what controls all health and healing in your body. A lot of misconceptions are out there. I'm sure you have your own. A major question I get, and I'm sure chiropractors all over get is, "Can you help me with _____."

Fill in the blank with, ear infections, back pain, headaches, diabetes, bunions, knee pain, numbness, cancer, high blood pressure, low blood pressure, infertility, you name it; I've been asked if chiropractic can help. Chiropractic does not cure anything. It does not fix your problem. The only goal, whether you come in with neck pain, diabetes, or headaches, is to find where you have interference to your nervous system and adjust that area to allow your body to function better. Let me ask you this question, "If I adjust you and remove the stress from your nerve system, and your digestive system starts working better, would that, in turn, help with constipation?" Or course. But that is not the goal to treat someone's health issue. It's all about removing the interference and letting God's healing power flow through you. Very often, when people are under regular chiropractic care, their health issues start going away. They need less medication. They feel better. They have more energy. They sleep better. They have fewer sick days. Why? They are merely healing better and moving toward God's principles of health and away from dis-ease. Chiropractic is not a treatment for anything. It aims to improve function. It's as simple as that, and it happens no other way. If you want your nervous system to function optimally, you should have your spine checked and adjusted by a good chiropractor regularly.

"I don't believe in chiropractic." Have you heard that before? Is that your thought? I love this! It is my favorite objection to chiropractic. Here's the thing, does it matter if you believe in gravity? Of course not, gravity does not care if you believe in it. If you jump off a building and deny gravity exists, what happens every time? SPLAT! Gravity wins. Because it is a law, a principle, it does not change according to your belief. The same goes for how your body functions and heals. Believe it or not, your brain and nerve system control everything in your body, and how well you're healing. Chiropractic is the vehicle that corrects your spine and nerve system, allowing your body to function and heal better. It's not a belief system. It's a law. Still don't believe it? Cut the nerve to your heart and see what happens. Just kidding, do NOT do that. Why? Your heart will stop. Think of Christopher Reeves. He damaged his spine and spinal cord, and his body shut down. The only difference between him and you is the amount of pressure you have on your spinal cord. Less is best. Everyone should have a good chiropractor to make sure they are functioning and healing God's way. Just as it says in John 15:5, "I am the vine; you are the branches. If you remain in me and I in you, you will bear much fruit; apart from me, you can do nothing. This is the chiropractic principle of life! God is our foundation, the source of all, just as is our brain and spinal cord. If we remain connected to God with as little interference as possible, we will prosper! We can do much through Him. If we stay connected as much as possible to our brain and spinal cord, our health will be abundant, and we will live with abundance! Separate ourselves from God, and there is no fruit. Separate ourselves from our nerve systems; there is no health.

We really cannot question the principle of chiropractic. Our bodies are designed to heal, made to heal, and always try to adapt and heal. This is a foundational principle for you to be healthy. You are designed by God to be healthy! He put all the power to heal you right inside of you already. Nothing outside can fix you. Your body needs to heal itself by removing as much interference as possible. Like gravity, this is a law, a principle. If we break laws, we pay the consequences. Here is what you can question, the application of chiropractic. Like all professions, like all doctors, there are flaws in the way that this principle is applied. I've known many different kinds of chiropractors. Some I would send my family to without hesitation; others I wouldn't want to send my worst enemy to get adjusted by them. The application is a worldly issue; the principle is a Godly issue. I encourage you not to dismiss this principle because of a past experience with a chiropractor or because you've heard of someone's experience. We are human. How we apply these principles of health and healing is what can change—question that. If you have had a poor experience, I apologize. That does not make these laws go away. Yes, chiropractic is safe, and yes, it is incredibly effective. When you work in conjunction with how God created our bodies and not work against it, amazing things can happen. They do happen. The principle remains. Question the application and find someone with whom you resonate and can give you excellent care. When you find that person, I promise that you will be healthier. You will function better. It's the way you were designed.

SUMMARY-TAKE 5

- Your brain and spinal cord control all function of your body and, therefore, control your health.
- Your spine, surrounds and protects your nerve system.
- Damage to your spine causes interference to your nervous system, causing disease.
- Chiropractic removes that interference allowing your body to heal better and improving function.
- Belief or Law? Regardless of your belief, this is how your body heals. Seek an excellent chiropractor to improve your health.

CHAPTER 6

TWO-THIRDS OF
GOD IS GO!

Ask, and it will be given to you; seek,
and you will find; knock, and it will be opened to you.
For everyone who asks receives, and the one who seeks finds,
and to the one who knocks it will be opened.

Matthew 7:7-8

We altered our mindsets quite a bit thus far about our health and how God fits in. You should see that there is a need to start doing things differently. If we just took a step back and looked around, we would see the need to pursue our health. As a healthcare provider, it becomes an almost daily task of conversing with patients who want a simple solution for their health problems. When I give them an answer that will, in my mind, undoubtedly provide them with relief and reversal of their issues, people will respond with, "OK, but do you have a supplement, or what about an Advil?" The point is, few people are willing to do what it takes to improve their health: commit to a long-term lifestyle shift. Most people want something quick and easy. They want something to fix and cure a problem they've lifestyled themselves into, something simple to reverse that problem overnight! We have to continue to alter our mindset that sickness and disease take time to develop, years in fact, and it takes time to restore health and healing to our bodies. In my experience, however, healing can happen a lot faster than the disease process, which is excellent news! The solution may be simple, but what are you willing to do to overcome your disease and restore health? Jeremiah 30:17 says, "But I will restore you to health and heal your wounds,' declares the LORD, 'because you are called an outcast, Zion for whom no one cares.'"As we begin to lean on Jesus and God's love for us more and more in all areas of our life, health included, He will renew and restore all things. This chapter is about the action we need to take in Christ, a step in faith.

I believe that people know that their bodies can heal and that they can be healthy. It just always seems like a daunting task to change their lifestyles. If there isn't an immediate correction, then they give up on themselves. They begin to fall back to the pattern of this world and seek a chemical fix, or just give up altogether. Even in the Christian world, we seek God, but when He doesn't "show up" and take all our problems away, we start looking elsewhere. We are people always searching for miracles, and we cease to create them in our own lives. We all have the lottery mentality. I'd love to win the lottery, you? I expect to win the lottery, but if I never have a ticket, my chances are impossible. We cannot have a lottery mentality with our health. There are no instant fixes. If you've tried to find one, it may help for a short time, but it is not long-lasting and life-changing.

Health issues arise because we come from a place of inaction or lacking proper action. It comes from a place of not wanting to do what it takes to experience a real change in our lives for the better. It comes from a place of just being OK enough not to want or have to change anything. God needs us to be stronger, healthier, and of clear mind. If we have a level of inaction throughout our lives, that inaction will breed sickness and disease, and, worse, a level of mediocrity that we do not qualify for in God's eyes. His perception of us is much greater than just living in a state of mediocrity.

In 2 Corinthians 5:7, Paul says, "For we walk by faith not by sight." And in Romans 8:24, he says, "for in this hope we were saved, but hope that is seen is no hope at all. Who hopes for what he can already see?"Both these scriptures depict what living in health and within God's laws of healing are all about. We know there needs to be an action in our faith. We are walking in a direction according to where God wants us and needs us to go. There is no sitting in faith. It doesn't say, "hang on and sit tight while faith happens to you."The second verse talks about hope. No one will hope for something they already have or can see. With our health, there needs to be both hope and action. Hebrews 6:19 says, "We have this hope as an anchor for the soul, firm and secure." If you want to experience God's gift of health and abundance, stop waiting, and begin to live in faith by taking action, expecting what we do will show up in our lives with abundance. Anchor to the fact that what we do to improve our health will undoubtedly create healing. We must at least buy a lottery ticket to get started.

Are you the kind of person who prays? If you're reading this book, then you probably are. You pray. I pray. The Bible says it's necessary; it's a way to communicate with God. Philippians 4:6 says, "Do not be anxious about anything, but in everything, by prayer and petition, with thanksgiving, present your requests to God." Psalm 145:18, says, "The Lord is near to all who call on him, to all who call on him in truth." 1 Thessolonians 5:17, "Pray without ceasing." James 5:13, "is anyone among you suffering? Let him pray. Is anyone cheerful? Let him sing praise."

Matthew 7:7-8, "Ask, and it will be given to you; seek, and you will find; knock, and it will be opened to you. For everyone who asks receives, and the one who seeks finds, and to the one who knocks it will be opened." I can only assume you pray when it comes to almost anything, including being healthy or praying for someone to overcome their disease. I know I do it a lot every day. Prayer helps. Prayer works. Prayer works even better when we pair it with action, and even better when we act according to God's laws and principles of health. It's especially important not to act according to the "laws" of this world. So how can we differentiate? Pray. I believe that God wants abundance for us, all of us. I also really believe that this world wants the opposite for us. The closer we are to God, the more steadfast we become in our prayer with God, the easier it becomes to separate the worldly views with God's purpose for us. Pray. Pray about everything. This is where we start to take action. I know I prayed for many things in my life, and I continually pray. I prayed about writing this book. Those prayers looked like this, "God, should I write this book? Will people want to read this?" Daily I prayed about this. Almost every day I prayed, I saw something about writing a book or got an email to write a book, yet I just ignored it. Eventually, I thought, *Oh, God's telling me the answer, write this book, people need to hear this message.* But it started with prayer and a thought in my mind and a purpose in my heart. We all have that feeling, but only with action can things happen. When we pair prayer and action, God shows up big time!

As a Christian, I find that I can live in faith, knowing that God is working diligently to work my life out. Although I may get in the way daily of His plan for me, He continues to work it out. Having faith and living faith can be two different things. It's especially evident when our health becomes compromised. We know in our spiritual minds that God is protecting us and keeping us safe, and His will is being done in our lives. But in our human minds, we are freaking out! What if something terrible happens, what if the test results are worse than we think? Will we make it out of the surgery? All these thoughts, which are the exact opposite of having faith, are thoughts of fear. Faith and fear work in opposition to each other. You cannot be living a faith-based life and be full of fear. When it comes to our lives, I believe we are either living in a faith-based system, knowing that God is taking care of us or living in a fear-based system where we have no idea what's happening next, and we are all doomed!

When it comes to your health, where do you live? Faith or fear? A little of both? More faith than fear? This is again our earthly dilemma. Remember Hebrews 11:1, "now faith is the substance of things hoped for, the evidence of things not seen" and it continues in verse 3, "by faith we understand that the worlds were framed by the word of God so that the things which are seen were not made of things which are visible." These verses define our health journey. We know and believe that God made us in His perfect image, that we need no help healing, just no interference. We are faithful that God lives in us and brings us health and healing. In the same breath, when something is diagnosed, we sprint from our faith-based system directly into a fear-based system. It's just our nature. Practicing faith is action. Fear is inaction. Being faithful is a walk; we walk by faith, not by sight. If we walked only in sight each day, we would all be in massive trouble. This world would eat us up and spit us out, not even thinking twice. When we live in fear, we tend to look for a simple way out, a quick way out. We act in a rash and fast way, not thinking clearly and hoping things work out. When we live in fear, and away from our God-given faith that He is our provider and our healer, fear takes over and overcomes our lives and our health even further. Faith is knowing God is with us, working all things out and acting as if He already has.

Some of my favorite stories on faith point out that action is necessary for us to overcome not just our health issues but all issues in our lives. If we are working on being more faithful, why not look at Jesus. He probably has some good advice on being faithful and overcoming and showing us that having faith comes with action. We all know Jesus' first miracle; how can we forget? It involves wine! Let's look at it. We know that Jesus and His disciples were invited to a wedding when the wine ran out. If you've ever been to a wedding when the wine runs out, there's a problem. Here, we see Jesus called to action by His mother. John Chapter 2 says, "And when they ran out of wine, the mother of Jesus said to Him, 'They have no wine.' At first,

Jesus responded to His mother like any young adult may react to his mother, and I'm paraphrasing, but He says something along the lines of, "that's not my problem!" His mother continues, knowing full well that eventually, her child will agree to what she is asking. She says in verse 5, "Whatever he says to you, do it." Let's stop there. When it comes to doing anything that may require a different action or a change in behavior, we are at first reluctant. A "No" is usually the first thing that comes out of our mouths. We think that it's too hard to do or that it won't work for us. Jesus seems to do this with His mother, responding the way we all might at first. But knowing who He is and why he's on this Earth, He agrees to listen and take action. The interesting thing in this story is that Jesus isn't really doing any of the work; He's telling people what to do. This miracle doesn't happen unless someone takes action. In verse 7, He says, "'Fill the waterpots with water, draw some out now, and take it to the master of the feast.' And they took it." Here we see that there was faith in action. Not inaction. A simple task of taking some jugs and putting water in them created a massive miracle that began a shift in the world. When it comes to our health, a simple change of thought and behavior will have an enormous transformation over time.

Luke Chapter 5, Jesus meets His disciples after they have been fishing all day with no luck. If you've ever been fishing and caught nothing after hours and hours, it's a rough day. So, Jesus gets on Simon's boat and says, "launch out into the deep and let down your nets for a catch." I'm sure just like we would have answered, Simon says, "but master, we have toiled all night and caught nothing; nevertheless, at your word, I will let down the net." At first, we are sk   eptical and unfaithful, but eventually, we know that God is at work, and He is who He says He is. The chapter continues saying, "and when they had done this, they caught a great number of fish, and their net was breaking." Our behavior is typically no different, even in our health. We know God wants us to be healthy, and we know at an earthly level he's watching over us, but we tend to act differently. We sit and wait for an answer rather than pursue His principles of health.

The miracles continue, and as it says in Matthew Chapter 8 verse 2, "A man with leprosy came and knelt before him and said, 'Lord, if you are willing, you can make me clean.' Jesus reached out his hand and touched the man. 'I am willing,' he said. 'Be clean!' Immediately he was cleansed of his leprosy. Then Jesus said to him, 'See that you don't tell anyone. But go, show yourself to the priest and offer the gift Moses commanded, as a testimony to them.'" Again, Jesus doesn't do much here in terms of healing this man. However, the man comes to Jesus fully faithful and takes a relatively large risk by running up to Jesus and falling to His feet. This man has leprosy! But in his faithfulness, he takes action, knowing that Jesus is who He says He is. The next move, Jesus tells the man that he must GO and show himself. When he takes action, the action that Jesus commands of him; he is healed. Again, in Luke Chapter 5, Jesus heals a paralyzed man. This miracle, to me, is what I think about when I know it's necessary to take action or take more action when moving to where God needs me. Verse 18, "Some men came carrying a paralyzed man on a mat and tried to take him into the house to lay him before Jesus. When they could not find a way to do this because of the crowd, they went up on the roof and lowered him on his mat through the tiles into the middle of the crowd, right in front of Jesus."

Let's start with this. If you knew that you were able to be healthy and God gave you a life to live to the max, how far would you go to achieve that? In this chapter, a paralyzed man is looking to be healed. They know Jesus is a healer, they have the faith, and now their action is pretty intense. At first, they don't succeed in getting in front of Jesus, so the man's friends lower him from the roof to land right in front of Jesus. I don't know about you, but if my friends were dropping me from a mat off a roof, I'd have my doubts. But this is what happens when faith meets action.

Verse 20, "When Jesus saw their faith, he said, 'Friend, your sins are forgiven.' The Pharisees and the teachers of the law began thinking to themselves, 'Who is this fellow who speaks blasphemy? Who can forgive sins but God alone?' Jesus knew what they were thinking and asked, 'Why are you thinking these things in your hearts? Which is easier: to say, "Your sins are forgiven," or to say, "Get up and walk"? But I want you to know that the Son of Man has authority on Earth to forgive sins.' So, he said to the paralyzed man, 'I tell you, get up, take your mat and go home.' Immediately he stood up in front of them, took what he had been lying on and went home praising God. Everyone was amazed and gave praise to God. They were filled with awe and said, 'We have seen remarkable things today.'"Because of this man's bold faith, he was healed. Again, not before there were other people around him speaking down to Jesus, being pessimistic, and trying to interfere with this man's faith. How often are you filled with faith and even begin taking action, and there's your spouse, friend, neighbor, or co-worker dragging you down to a level of no hope? This man stayed faithful, he didn't waiver, and Jesus tells him to get up, take his mat and GO! I feel in this story, Jesus has a little fire in Him. But not upset, convicted. He never has to convince anyone of anything. He is convicted of who He is and why He's there. When your bold faith meets Jesus' conviction, there is no stopping you, even if the world tells you otherwise. This story also shows how important your "inner circle" of friends can be. Surround yourself with people who will raise you (in this story, lower you down), always supporting you in your journey.

This last example of how we need to begin taking action in our life and our health, to walk in faith, defines our lives today and the questions we ask about our health. It starts in John chapter 9, the story of Jesus healing a blind man. "As he went along, he saw a man blind from birth. His disciples asked him, 'Rabbi, who sinned, this man or his parents, that he was born blind?'These first few verses speak volumes on how we perceive our health and our lives today. Why did God do this to me? Why did He let my child have a health issue? Why didn't He do this or that? We ask the same questions that people ask thousands of years ago when it comes to our situation and our health. Why did God do this? What did I do to deserve this? Jesus quickly responds with what we all need to hear, "'Neither this man nor his parents sinned,' said Jesus, 'but this happened so that the works of God might be displayed in him.'"You didn't do anything wrong. But Jesus again responds with a statement that blows our perspective of health clearly out of the water, and it's worth repeating, "this happened so that the works of God might be displayed in him." Whoa! This perspective of our health should completely alter any view we have had in terms of our health. God may allow something to show up in your life so that He can intervene, and His glory and power can be shown through you. He allows things to happen so that He can do the healing. Jesus continues, "'As long as it is day, we must do the work of him who sent me. Night is coming when no one can work. While I am in the world, I am the light of the world.' After saying this, he spit on the ground, made some mud with the saliva, and put it on the man›s eyes."Jesus now gets to work. He begins the miracle of healing this man, spitting in the dirt and making mud. Now, if you close your eyes and hear someone hocking up a loogy, and then all of a sudden you feel this cold, wet paste being smeared over your face, you may feel a little confused, but probably grossed out even if it's Jesus' spit. But here is the essential part of the story. The next verse continues with the action. "'Go,' he told him, 'wash in the Pool of Siloam.' So the man went and washed and came home seeing. His neighbors and those who had formerly seen him begging asked, 'Isn't this the same man who used to sit and beg?' Some claimed that he was. Others said, 'No, he only looks like him.' But he insisted, 'I am the man.' 'How then were your eyes opened?' they asked. He replied, 'The man they call Jesus made some mud and put it on my eyes. He told me to go to Siloam and wash. So, I went and washed, and then I could see."'First, I like how the man leaves out the part where Jesus made the mud out of spit, but that's a little irrelevant. Secondly, and most importantly, Jesus commanded him to, "Go." Go take this action, and you will see. The importance of first having faith, and then linking that faith with proper action makes all the difference. Walking the walk of faith leads to healing. Let God show up in your life, let Him change your life and your ability to heal with abundance by taking God's action. It's important to know that your healing begins when you have the faith to know that God is working in your life to help you and to heal you. Then, when you pair your faith with proper action, this leads to abundance in health. You may begin to feel uplifted after reading through those Bible verses and seeing how God shows up when we take action in our health and our lives. However, there typically comes a time when you say, "but." "But I don't have time to take action; my life is so busy right now." Can you hear yourself saying things like this? "I'm too tired to take action. I'm in too much pain and don't have the energy to do anything I know is good for me."

How big is your, but? "I know I need to start doing things differently, but not right now." I've heard this so many times from people that they can't get healthy and begin something now; it's not the right time. They don't have money right now, but maybe in the new year, they'll start something. What exactly are they waiting for? The last I checked it's never a good time to be unhealthy, it's never a good time to have to fight cancer or diabetes or headaches or heart disease! But by postponing getting healthy and taking action in that, they're choosing to allow the disease process to infiltrate their lives slowly. Sickness doesn't wait for anyone. It's happening now whether we think so or not. Do not wait. Do not push off what can be started today. The longer you wait, the more difficult it is to get healthy.

Don't let your but get any bigger. Do not let your but get in the way of your purpose and your health. There's some good news in this; we're working with God here. God gives grace.

God's grace extends to all areas of our lives. We've been given the gift of eternal life through Jesus' death and resurrection. Ephesians 2:8-9, "For it is by grace that you have been saved, through faith, and this is not from yourselves, it is the gift of God, not by works, so that no one can boast." Our eternal souls are well taken care of because there is nothing we can do to earn it. When it comes to our physical bodies, grace is extended as well. When we look around to a sick and suffering, unhealthy world, it's a miracle that our bodies don't just shut down and die way before they're supposed to. With all the bad food, fast food, toxic chemicals sprayed on everything, the lack of physical activity, smoking, medications, depression, it's a miracle that can only be chalked up to God's grace in our physical health that we are still alive! Think about that. With all the stuff that we know is extremely unhealthy for us, we still survive. See, God created our bodies to live. When we honor that principle and take action, we not only live, but undoubtedly, we thrive.

Let God extend His grace into your life. You do not need to move any mountains today, or even tomorrow. This mentality is where we fall short. Thinking we need to get our health back today is not how it works. We do not lose our health in a day, so stop trying to get it back in a day. Remember, God needs no help healing you. He just needs no interference. I'll even amend that and say, He needs less interference. Allow God to work in your life. Begin moving pebbles, not mountains. And if you haven't worked out in a while, moving pebbles is a lot easier than trying to move mountains. Let God do your heavy lifting. We just need to start taking the appropriate action so that God can work. "Come to me, all who labor and are heavy laden, and I will give you rest. Take my yoke upon you and learn from me, for I am gentle and lowly in heart, and you will find rest for your souls. For my yoke is easy, and my burden is light." Matthew 11:28-30. "He saved us, not because of works done by us in righteousness, but according to his mercy, by the washing of regeneration and renewal of the Holy Spirit." Titus 3:5 "Don't be afraid, for I am with you. Don't be discouraged, for I am your God. I will strengthen you and help you. I will hold you up with my victorious right hand." Isaiah 41:10 In all things, lean on God. In your health, lean on God. We all have burdens and doubts that pull us further away from our purpose and our health. We often look to this world for answers when the answers are with Him. Let's begin to act according to Him, and He will show up. You will have abundance, your nets will be full, and you will see more clearly than ever before. You just need to get over your paralysis and Go.

SUMMARY-TAKE 5

- To have what you want, to truly be healthy, you must take action.
- Pairing faith in God with the proper action leads to abundance.
- God's grace extends to your health.
- Do not let your "but" get in the way.
- Look to God, lean on Him in all things, in health, and remember to, "Go!"

CHAPTER 7

YOUR PURPOSE
IN THIS JOURNEY

I cry out to God Most High, to God who fulfills his purpose for me. Psalm 57:2 We know that in all things God works for good with those who love him, those whom he has called according to his purpose.

Romans 8:28

To continue with the theme of our last chapter, you need to begin changing how you think about your health. Often, I will consult with someone, or they'll come to a health talk, and afterward, they'll say something along the lines of, "That was great, and I know I need to start doing something about my health, but it's just not the right time. I'm starting a new job, the holidays are coming up, and money is tight." Maybe you've thought those thoughts too. I know I have. I will quickly ask that person, or even myself, "How important is your health, and for you to be healthy?" A typical answer should be, "It's imperative. Without my health, I really cannot do the things I need to do or want to do. I cannot be a great spouse, parent, co-worker, or follower of Christ." Exactly. Because it is not yet a crisis, we believe in our minds that we have time to gather our things and wait for the perfect time to start changing our behavior to a healthier, God-focused lifestyle. Again, there is never a good time to get sick or develop a disease. But it's happening to you now unless you take action to build health.

If you were to ask one hundred people with cancer, diabetes, or heart disease, "How did you feel before the diagnosis?" They may all say, "I felt fine." See, there is never a perfect time to begin getting healthy; I promise you that. The only perfect time is after we get sick. At that point, we have to make a shift. Then, all of a sudden, we have the time and money and everything changes in an instant. Why do we have to wait for a crisis to believe we need to shift our healthcare finally? Let's act as if we have no choice but to change how our bodies are healing and functioning BEFORE a crisis occurs.

The main reason why we wait or disregard our internal dialogue to start taking action is because we're inherently selfish. Now, don't take this the wrong way, but we are. I see this, especially in our health. If you have a family, it's easy to work long hours and sacrifice your time at home with your spouse and children to make money and make sure they're taken care of. Of course, that's important and a noble thing to do. I have a young son, and I know if I leave for my office hours, he's not wanting me to go and pleading for me to stay. Of course, I know I need to work, and working is my responsibility, but he would rather have me home spending time with him. Working is important. But when we put other things ahead of what's more important in the name of making more money, or spending time away from the things that you're trying to protect, or put off your health until later are all selfish acts. I'm not saying that it's wrong, but we need to identify what we're working for and WHY we're doing it. Think about this. The life you've been gifted is not meant to be lived for yourself. This life is not about you! So, when someone tells me that they don't have time to take care of their health and that it hurts too much to exercise and they can't find the money to eat well or get under care to correct their nervous systems, it's selfish. The selfless act would be doing the opposite of those things. Start putting the people you do life with ahead of yourself. Your life is meant to be shared with your spouse, your children, family, and friends. You are an integral part of their lives, so start investing in yourself to have the life God gave you and wants for you. Endure the pain and being uncomfortable to be able to live like you were intended.

Where to start? You must determine the "WHY" God put in your heart? This is a crucial action step. Identify your WHY. If you can do this, then the HOW is simple. With a reason for doing anything, especially to developing yourself to become a stronger, healthier child of God, you'll be able to endure the difficulties that come with becoming healthier. Many people will initially say that their "why" is to be a great parent and be there for their children. Absolutely. But that's what they're supposed to do, not their God-given purpose. To be able to be a great and present parent, you must be healthy, so use that in your walk toward health. To clarify that point, what happens when your kids grow up? Do you still walk them to their college classes, go on their honeymoon with them? Always clean and maintain their rooms? You get the point. Be a great parent. But that's not your purpose; it's not your why. To find your why, try the following exercise.

If money weren't an issue, you needed nothing else, never had to work again in your life to make money, what would you do? I know, at first, you'd do nothing or go on a wild vacation for a month with all your friends; I would too! But after that, you come home, what does that look like? You have to do something. Perhaps you'd quit your job. Maybe you'd move. What would you do if you didn't have to do anything? I'll give you my personal why and how I can stay anchored to it. I truly believe God put me on the path I'm on to use me to help others achieve their God-given potential in life through His principles of health, even through this book I was called to write. I'm not a writer, but here we are. If I never had to work again, I would still be in my office, adjusting people, doing workshops on health, going to churches to speak. Why? Because it's my purpose, and my WHY is to make sure that this world is a better place for people to know and love Jesus and to serve something greater than myself. My family is a part of this mission and purpose. I don't exclude them from my why and my purpose; they're a part of it. When I need to leave for my office or have a health consultation that takes me away from my son and wife, they know that I'm going to help people, but I'll be back soon to play tackle with my son, building blocks, or do a puzzle. But now, it's time to work.

It's easy to walk your why when it's part of your job, and you get paid for it. That's the goal. However, many of us aren't living a why we get paid for. Continue to work, but keep searching for your why, your purpose in this world. Remember to put God in the center of your life, and start making decisions about your life with Him in the middle. Begin to remove the interferences in your life that are pulling you away from your why and your purpose. I know you have those things that you enjoy doing that are costing you an abundance of time and money, pulling you away from your God-given potential. These things are usually the same things that are costing you time and money from getting healthy.

Pray about your why. Do the exercise of what you would do if you no longer had to work. That will usually put something in your heart that you can feel; that's God speaking to you. The less interference you have in your life, the clearer that voice becomes.

Back to not being selfish for a moment. Once your why becomes more apparent, and the clearer it is, the stronger it is and the easier it is to stay the course for your health. Without a why and a purpose, we can anchor to nothing. We float around life with nothing to secure us to the things we find important. If we don't anchor to anything, then we'll falsely anchor to anything. We don't have this life for ourselves, but it's a gift to share with others and the world. Imagine if Jesus just kept to himself and just did whatever He wanted. He just stayed on the down-low. Never pushed buttons. He never performed a miracle, except the ones He could benefit from. This life is not about you. I've seen too often that a husband or wife will come to see me, and they're on the path of self-destruction, their health is failing, and they have nearly given up. The system has failed them, and they've lost their way. They could almost go either way, live or die, makes no difference. IT DOES MAKE A DIFFERENCE! Do you recall Romans Chapter 8? Verse 37? "Yet in all these things we are more than conquerors through him who loved us." When you have no why, and you forget who created you, then this world takes you down. We must anchor to God and the power He put inside our bodies to be more than conquerors! You don't have a spirit of weakness but a spirit of strength! If you're a Christian, you have the power of Jesus, who conquered death! And you want to give up? Throw in the towel? Listen to the doctors who say that there's nothing else they can do! What do they know? They know of earthly things, not of heavenly things. Not in the power that made your body! I've seen people heal when all other doctors had given up. But there was a spirit of being more than a conqueror in those people, and they got well.

Do not conform to the pattern of this world. It's out to destroy you. It will come after your health, and everything else will begin to fall apart. Don't live for yourself, but live for others. Live for the purpose that God has gifted you. When you have your health, when you're on the path toward living and not just being alive, an abundance mentality joins you. Don't wait to be healthy. Don't put things off that are of most importance until later. We already agreed, your health is of utmost importance. Anchor yourself to your "why," and you'll be able to endure any "how."

"Come to me, all who labor and are heavy laden, and I will give you rest. Take my yoke upon you and learn from me, for I am gentle and lowly in heart, and you will find rest for your souls. For my yoke is easy, and my burden is light" Matthew 11:28-30Put your stress and your history of shortcomings onto him. "Cast your burden on the Lord, and he shall sustain you; he shall never permit the righteous to be shaken." Psalm 55:22

SUMMARY-TAKE 5

- This gift of your life is not meant only for you; it's meant to be shared.
- You must determine what your "why" is to succeed in your health journey. Make it a meaningful "why."
- You must act selflessly in health. Continue to anchor to your why every day.
- You are more than a conqueror. You have been called to overcome!
- Put your burdens on God. Surround yourself with others with like-minds. He will sustain you.

CHAPTER 8

LIVING BY FAITH

Trust in the Lord with all your heart,
and do not lean on your own understanding.
In all ways acknowledge him,
and he will make straight your paths.

Proverbs 3:5-6

Now faith is being sure of what we hope for
and certain of what we do not see.

Hebrews 11:1

Our health needs to be at the very core of what we do, or our lives will not be fully lived. When we begin to change how we view our health, we can then start to manage it differently. I completely understand that because of all the information we have at our fingertips, knowing what health is and how to attain it can be complicated. Remember in Hosea 4:6, "My people are destroyed for lack of knowledge." We all want better health, and I hope by now, we understand that health does not come to us by luck or passed down through genetics. How we live and act allows our bodies to either build health or disease. Which do you prefer? I'm assuming we all want more health, more abundance in living, and tapping into our God-given potential.

In Chapter 4, we learned that health is not just feeling a certain way but also how your body is performing, how it functions and heals. I find with people, this is a relatively easy concept to grasp, but it becomes the most difficult to walk out. Health is an action. There's just no way around it. One of my patients, Adam, who came to me complaining of persistent back pain. After a few days of his back pain not improving, I sent him for additional testing, which revealed a small cyst on or near his kidney, which the doctors said not to worry. Of course, he worries, and I understand that. He initially came to see me after I spoke at his church about health and living with abundance. He was on disability for over three months because he developed three bulging discs in his neck that caused severe pain, numbness, and tingling into his right arm and hand. His doctors initially gave him significant medications to block the pain, but all drugs came with side effects he didn't want. His next options were spinal injections that would also aim to block the pain, but not resolve the bulging discs. He decided to take action and consult me. He was in a tough place. His condition was getting worse, he couldn't work or take care of his family like he wanted to, and taking drugs and doing the surgery wasn't on his top priority list. He was desperate. Why does our health take last priority until it has to be a top priority? We all know we need to do better. We all know we can't wait for a crisis to begin changing our health. Yet we still do! We wait! Paul describes our behavior in Romans 7:15-20, "I do not understand what I do. For what I want to do, I do not do, but what I hate I do. And if I do what I do not want to do, I agree that the law is good. As it is, it is no longer I myself who do it, but it is sin living in me. For I know that good itself does not dwell in me, that is, in my sinful nature. For I have the desire to do what is good, but I cannot carry it out. For I do not do the good I want to do, but the evil I do not want to do—this I keep on doing. Now if I do what I do not want to do, it is no longer I who do it, but it is sin living in me that does it."

We know we need to do differently and be better and committed to our health so that we can live the best most abundant life we can, yet we don't do it.

After I laid out a very detailed plan to help Adam correct his spine and disc problems, he committed to his health and was all in on what I asked of him. I chose his story because it's not unlike yours. When a problem arises, we tend to deal with it more quickly. When it's more of a problem, we tend to deal with it even quicker; we choose to change as much as we can as soon as we can. See, Adam was a patient of mine a few years before he re-entered my office. He did well, but after about six months of care, he felt he didn't need to continue. Fast forward almost four years later and Adam comes back to my office with a near-surgical-related problem. If he had continued with his care and kept doing the things that built his health, he would not have been in this situation. However, because God brought him here, He'll bring him through it. Adam began getting adjusted again, and, this time, it was a lot more frequent and for longer. Within a few weeks, he was feeling better with less pain, numbness, tingling and with fewer symptoms of bulging discs. Since re-starting, he is near normal with no medications and no surgery needed. This time around, he has continued care and isn't looking to quit. Adam's story won't end poorly as long as he continues pursuing his health. His cyst is where faith meets action. Our bodies are designed by God to heal and be well.

Adam is healing. But, now, this cyst happens. All of a sudden, he begins to question what he should do. Surgery? Get that thing sucked out by a huge needle. Leave it? More and more questions popped up. Although his doctors advised him not to worry, he worries; we all would. But this is no different than any other problem we develop. The body allowed this thing to grow, so let's start getting our body healthier. Let's stop trying to treat and just cut things off; we need to take action to build health, not just treat a symptom. Adam trusted that God made his body for health when it came to his neck issues, but he quickly began to question if his body was able to heal the cyst.

He found it easy to come to see me to get adjusted, but he was finding it difficult to change other areas of his health when it came to the cyst. He was questioning whether or not he should improve his nutrition or start exercising. He was having difficulty with his mindset. We stopped and had a consultation. We discussed putting God back in the center of his life. Adam is a faithful Christian, but like we all do, he questioned his faith when things get hard. He was back in my office more frequently to help maintain accountability. He had hope and an understanding that his body is indeed able to heal, but he needed to take action to regain his health. If his neck can heal, so can this. He came to understand that he needed to take more to restore health and not wait anymore to have this issue get more out of control. We made a plan he could start that day. But it won't work unless he implements it.

Before we get into specifics of what action is appropriate and what will last, we need to understand what doesn't work. Or which actions may be hindering you from health and healing.

As I've said before, a lot of information is out there, and you can easily find what you're looking for, good and bad. We know fad diets will come and go. Fad workout routines will get you to pay hundreds of dollars a month, and they only last for a few weeks before you get bored of it. The next health guru with the next best-selling supplement will guarantee that your libido and energy levels will be through the roof. There will always be the next big thing that will help empty your pockets, while not being able to be sustained in your life or with peaking results. We have all been caught up in something like this, or have been fooled into some multilevel marketing promotion that promises tons of money if you just sign up now! Although these diets and exercises may help, can you sustain them for your entire life? Are you willing to? Remember, a lot of these infomercials and doctors promise to help you lose weight, and get your memory back, or take away your knee pain, or whatever it is, but it's always the easy way out. Just take this! It's no different than our medical industry. If you have a pain or symptom, take this drug. It's all about making money while giving you some sort of relief for a short time. Like our God, we're looking for long-term, sustainable health that won't fail. I think it's important to remember that this world is out to take us down. The enemy is out to find you and destroy you in any way possible. When we focus our lives around God and His principles, we take our focus off the world and place it on God, where it belongs. We can then make more appropriate decisions for our lives, including our health.

As we begin to shift our mindset toward true health and away from all the fad diets and exercise routines and workout equipment, away from the world's view on health, and onto

God's way of health, we need to know that God is full of grace, even in our health. We are all familiar with the scripture saying that we are all saved by grace and not by works, or we cannot do enough good to make it to heaven; it is purely on God's love for us that we have an eternal life. As in Acts 15:11, "No! We believe it is through the grace of our Lord Jesus that we are saved, just as we are." In Titus 2:11, "For the grace of God has appeared that offers salvation to all people." Eternal grace is an incredible gift. We don't have to do anything to earn it. I believe that that grace extends toward our health, but the difference becomes that it is by works that we achieve abundant health. The great news is, God created our bodies so well, that we indeed are "fearfully and wonderfully made," Psalm 139:14, that we simply need to honor that and health will be achieved.

Now, you may be reading this and thinking, "This seems great, but I'm so far gone that I don't stand a chance." Maybe you think that you don't even know what to do, so you do nothing. Perhaps you're like me a lot of the time and want to do so much and do more but end up falling short. I'm here to tell you that because God's grace extends further than your spiritual health, all you need to do is to begin moving in His direction, let His design do the rest. You're in a marathon, not a sprint. Have hope, if you remember back in the chiropractic chapter, the brain and nervous system control and coordinate all functions in the body. Often, a new patient will come to see me with a symptom that has been with them for years. Very often, it's lower back pain or headaches. These symptoms are not normal! They are, however, extremely common. After dealing with these problems for years and being put on all sorts of treatments and medications, they wind up in my office or an office like mine. We teach them how their body works and how they're designed to heal; after all, God did put the most incredible healing potential in your body. What I usually find is damage to their spine and, therefore, their nervous system, so they are not healing at 100%. It takes time to correct someone's spine, but the truth is you don't need perfection for improved function and health. That's the great news! You don't need perfection to be healthy with God's grace in our health! After one or maybe a few adjustments within a set amount of time, that person begins to feel relief. It's particularly special when someone has dealt with headaches or another common issue daily, and after a few adjustments to their nervous system, they realize their problem is significantly less painful or gone altogether. By no means are they completely healed or completely perfect; there's just a little more healing happening, this is good news for us. We just need to move in the right direction, and our bodies will begin healing; it works all the time.

Something else that makes us fall short in our health is praying that our bad actions are miraculously transmuted. I know we've all prayed this prayer, "Dear Jesus, thank you for all you've given us." So far so good, but then this happens, "Please let this fried chicken and ice cream and cake for dessert and a diet coke to wash it all down miraculously nourish my body so that I may be healthy." Here's the real miracle; He created a body that can take in artificial flavors, colors, badly damaged fats, man-made chemicals, toxins, and whatever else is in our "food" these days and somehow break it down as best it can and give you some kind of nourishment. Eating that kind of food will provide you with a longer life than eating nothing. Think about that. You can eat, drink, and smoke, and, somehow, your intelligently designed body will, in a miraculous way, adapt and keep you alive! However, your life isn't about just surviving and being kept alive; it's about thriving, anchoring your behavior to God's principles of health and healing so that you may have life and live it abundantly. Live according to the law and quit hoping for a miracle when you've been living against the laws that God has governed us with.

Think about this again, we can avoid working out regularly, eat horrible foods, smoke, drink, be miserable and stressed out, have a damaged and degenerative spine, yet our bodies will still find ways to keep us alive. We live this real miracle daily. A miracle is something that nature cannot explain. It's like jumping out of a plane without a parachute and somehow living. That would be a miracle against natural law. Our bodies will adapt for a long time; however, we are either building health or creating disease. It's one direction or the other. Don't be fooled by a lack of diagnosis to think you're perfectly healthy if you're living a life that's not conducive to building health within the natural laws of our body. In reading through the Bible about this type of behavior, I came across Hebrews 13:9, and it couldn't be more perfect, "Do not be carried away by all kinds of strange teachings. It is good for our hearts to be strengthened by grace, not by eating ceremonial foods, which is of no benefit to those who do so." Ceremonial foods! We're always trying to celebrate something, aren't we? The cakes and desserts, the "vacation meals" six times a week! We know these aren't bringing us closer to health, only further away.

Here's the good news; there's always good news when we cling to God's way of life. You don't need to be perfect to see a result or even begin to get healthier. Remember, there's grace when we start moving in the right direction. There's still plenty of room for error, but we need to step in the right direction. Just as we decide and begin to change our lifestyle, we instantly function and heal better. That's God's grace in our health, in the body He designed for us to live. An immediate health response occurs. It's just like when you decide to be a Christian and follow Jesus. All you need to do is begin by turning toward Him and begin taking the steps to live for Him. In an instant, your eternal life is changed. But it doesn't mean your physical life is perfect, the work has only begun. But daily, when we choose Christ, we're walking toward a more perfect life that He has in store for us. As we dive deeper into the specifics of what an actual healthy lifestyle is, don't get overwhelmed. We all need to build up our strength in what we're able and willing to tolerate. There's nothing that can be gained without some form of stress. We build muscle by stressing them. Our mind is strengthened by pushing it to its limit and then just past it. Although we all want to have perfection with our health, we need to understand that you don't fully achieve full health. We are continuously looking only to get better. To continue the journey, one step at a time and grow better and stronger and healthier while cementing our principles to God's way of life for us. All it takes is for you to decide which direction your life will go. Will you continue the same path you're on, relying on modern medicine to find you that cure? Will you continue eating the way you do and not being active? Will you continue to let your mind go to places that you never wanted them to go to? If you're ready, here's the best part: it only requires you to do simple things, daily. Let God's incredible design do the rest. Are you ready to jump? Psalm 142:3 "When my spirit was overwhelmed within me, then you knew my path. In the way in which I walk, they have secretly set a snare for me." There is a point right before we do anything worthwhile when we feel insecure and almost burdened. A snare. A tangle. Then a force of guidance telling us to go, to do, to take that action. When God is at the core, that burden is light, and the path becomes clear. Now jump.

SUMMARY-TAKE 5

- You are wonderfully made, by God, for God. You are made to be healthy!
- Anchor to a sustainable health system that always works and never fails: God's.
- Don't be taken by fad diets and expensive exercise equipment. They don't last.
- God's grace extends to your health; you don't need to be perfect to get started.
- Don't be burdened in this; cast your fears and doubts onto Him. He will make your path clear.

CHAPTER 9

THE JUMP

No temptation has overtaken you that is not common to man. God is faithful, and he will not let you be tempted beyond your ability, but with the temptation, he will also provide the way of escape, that you may be able to endure it.

1 Corinthians 10:13

Let's work with our bodies, not against them. When we do that, the results are incredible! When we're walking in the same direction God wants us to go, the burden is light, and our health is extraordinary. Now, how in the world can we distinguish what we should be doing to achieve health and what we shouldn't be doing? As I've said before, there is a ton of information and not a lot of actual longevity to our health foundation. Diets come and go. Supplements are a dime a dozen (although, I would recommend some supplements). Medications are continually being recalled for causing severe health problems. Workouts and the equipment sold with them come and go... So now what?

Remember what health is? How your body is healing and functioning. Now, all we need to do is aid our bodies in improving its ability to function, the way God intended it to do. It isn't all that complicated. The truth never really is, is it? Let's start at the top.Our Mindset

Colossians 3:2, "Set your minds on things that are above, not on things that are on earth."Romans 12:2, "Do not be conformed to this world, but be transformed by the renewal of your mind, that by testing you may discern what the will of God is, what is good and acceptable and perfect."1 Corinthians 14:33, "For God is not a God of confusion, but of peace."Have you ever thought about how important your mind is to your overall health? Have you ever been so stressed out that you've become sick? Have you ever woken up from a dream with your heart racing? Perhaps that's the most exercise some of us get. Our thoughts turn into reality. Have you had a dream about your spouse that caused you to wake up mad at them? A literal dream that has no bearing on reality caused you to wake up angry at your spouse! The mind is a substantial factor in our health. We must protect it. This is where we need to start when it comes to our overall health. Throughout the Bible, you can find verses about our mindset and focusing our minds not on things of this world but on God. I believe this is one of the most challenging aspects of our health to maintain. Why? Take a quick look at your day. You wake up and perhaps like most people, you check your phone, go on social media, or even put on the TV to see what's happening in the world. How often is a news channel promoting something good? Political scandals. Who killed who? Natural disaster leading to thousands homeless. Robberies, death, warnings of pedophiles, and people who are armed and dangerous, and viruses that are taking over the world. It becomes ridiculous! You can't make up how bad this world is. Social media isn't a whole lot better. We may not see all the negativity on social media; we see everyone else's most amazing moments, and we compare them to our own lives and get depressed over how much we don't have. It becomes challenging to get a grasp of what's real and what isn't. So, again, we need to put God back into everything we do and focus back on Him in our lives.

Action Step 1: Wake up grateful. God has already given you so much. When in doubt, look up positive Bible verses that mean something to you. Read something that motivates you or inspires you. I respond better to uplifting music in the morning. I need to get my physical body moving, and music helps to do that. Then I can get focused on reading or writing/journaling. Whatever works for you, do that. But do not dive right into the pattern of this world; it alters your sense of reality and brings you further away from your God-given potential. Protect your mental state. Anchor to God. Even at work! What keeps your mind sharp and stable during a day that is full of things pulling you off purpose? I recommend getting back to a solid mental state multiple times per day. Refocus. We need to continually be aware of our mindset, the mental state we are in. When we get taken away from that steady-state, negativity and worldly views can attack us. Keep your mindset secure. Anchor to God's way, not the world's way.   Tan Lines: This is a concept that helps me keep doing what I do and why I do it. Life is complicated. Our day-to-day living can be like surviving—living paycheck to paycheck. We survive the week to get to the weekend. Spouse issues, kid issues, feeling less than we're born to be, and then we add in our failing health. It's hard. We get stuck in this rut of surviving and not truly living, very much like our health and our healthcare system. Once we're in it, it's difficult to claw our way out. The sooner we realize we're off track, the quicker we can get back on the right course and back to living with abundance. Are you this kind of person? Are you stuck in a survival mode? I know there are times that I am, it's natural. It's OK. The key is to realize we're in a survival state and then get out. In some areas of our lives, it's almost a good thing to be in a survival state. Why? When we're in a survival state, we work harder. Our focus gets clearer; we establish plans to get out of the situation, but only after we've had time to assess what's happening. If your marriage is failing and you get divorce papers out of the blue, you get in survival mode. "What can I do? Let's have a date night! Let's get counseling!" All the things you should have been doing already are now a priority. The same goes for your health. Don't wait to be in a place of survival, but if you are, do whatever it takes to survive, then course correct so you don't end up there again. So how do tan lines come into play? Have you ever been on vacation before? I hope you have. If not, I'm inviting you to take one. Some of the highest highs in my life have been on family vacations throughout my life. I remember the times we've had. Not necessarily the things we got, but the people I was with and the places we got to see. Often, we don't travel very far. It can even be a staycation. My favorite spot is by the beach, with plenty of sun with my family. I know we become overdue as a family when our tan lines start to fade. Not necessarily literally, but it is a good indicator that we need to stop. See how life is going. Are we getting closer to a goal or getting too far off course? I'm not suggesting taking a vacation every weekend, but the key is to have something to look forward to. What are your tan lines? What refreshes you to keep going and stay inspired? Maybe you hate the beach. What allows you to vacate the day-to-day and look ahead to something that brings more life to you? Here's what tan lines mean: have something on your calendar that you look forward to. It doesn't have to be eight months from now and cost you $5,000; it can be something small, a night out. But something you can see in the distance that you're working toward, a reward. If you can plan something a bit more extraordinary, great! But it doesn't need to be expensive. Some of the best times we've had, more recently, are when we spend the least amount of money. The point is always to be looking forward to something. It keeps us going in the direction we want to go where God needs us. Psalm 37:4 says, "delight yourself in the Lord, and he will give you the desires of your heart." Stay committed to him, look up, keep your mind secure and focused. Life is full of abundance; we just need to open our eyes and keep moving forward. Find your tan lines. Let's Get Physical!

"Therefore, I urge you, brothers and sisters, because of God's mercy, to offer your bodies as a living sacrifice, holy and pleasing to God—this is your true and proper worship. Romans 12:1

Do you not know that your bodies are temples of the Holy Spirit, who is in you, whom you have received from God? You are not your own; you were bought at a price. Therefore honor God with your bodies." 1 Corinthians 16:19-20"She sets about her work vigorously; her arms are strong for her tasks." Proverbs 31:17"But those who hope in the Lord will renew their strength. They will soar on wings like eagles; they will run and not grow weary, they will walk and not be faint." Isaiah 40:31

Action Step 2: A good deal of our health will be related to our mindset and what we're willing to do to keep our heads in the game. If our mindset is poor, we'll find excuses. If our why and our anchor is steadfast in our God-given purpose, we'll find a way. As you develop your mind, your body will need to follow. If we are to be true stewards of God and live out our purpose, our physical bodies need to be reliable. No, you do not need to be an Olympic weightlifter or a record-setting long-distance runner, you just need to get moving, physically. In this section, I'll help you get moving in such a simple way; all your excuses will no longer be valid. God made us to be physical beings. He built us to bend and lift and run and jump. I often look at my son and see what his body is doing. I believe he's closer to God than I am. What is he wanting or needing to do? Often, it's to go outside and play. Play on the swing set! Play baseball! Play tackle! Play. So, play we do. Here's the thing. If you, as a parent or child, or grandparent, are not physically fit to do something, you can easily make an excuse not to do something. In this section of getting physical, no matter your limits, you'll be able to get moving to build your strength, stamina, and endurance. Not because you want to, but because you are a God-loving, God-fearing person who is honoring your savior with your body. It's that simple. Honor God through the temple He built for you. Stop burning it down with inadequate food, medications, inactivity, and "woe is me" mentality, full of excuses.

Now, you may not like me. If you're a child of God, and you are, He died for you. By not taking care of our physical bodies and using them for good and to honor God, we're robbing ourselves of abundance! I've heard all the excuses before! My knee! My back! I'm too far gone! I can't get up! I'm too old! You don't need to be perfectly fit or entirely ready to get started; you just need to start! The purpose of exercising isn't necessarily to help you lose weight or fit into your pants better. It's not even to make you look good in a bathing suit; it helps, but that's not why I exercise. That's not the "why" you should have either. Those reasons are lame and selfish. Remember, it's not about you! Let's get back to living for God and for those around us whom you care about. Those people who need you to be able and active! Be the 90-year-old still running and jumping with your great-grandkids, tiring them out!

I know I don't have to explain the benefits of exercise, do I? Well, I'll explain just a few benefits, at least. Regular exercise helps in increasing your mood (reversing depression), aids in weight loss, builds muscle and burns fat, increases oxygen uptake, increases energy, reverses chronic disease, helps brain function and memory, improves sleep, minimizes arthritis symptoms, and reduces risk of stroke and practically every cancer! These are just a few of the benefits! If knowing that God created our bodies to be strong and fit wasn't enough and caused us to take action, then hopefully, science will help us get moving. Think about this for a minute; if there was a drug or food that would help fix and cure depression, increase your energy, help you lose weight, reduce cancer and stroke risk, reverse diabetes, and improve your brain function, would you take it? How much would you pay for it? And what if it was in the same drug?! It would be the best-selling and probably the most expensive medicines of all time. So, if we know all the incredible benefits of exercise and that our bodies are made and meant to move and be active, why don't we exercise? We'll do anything to avoid working out. We avoid the discomfort of exercise. We enter a vicious cycle until the cycle just turns into our sedentary life, just the way the enemy wants it. He wants you to be stuck in the same place and allow you to believe everything is fine just the way it is. Is that who you are? Have you allowed yourself to believe that you aren't a "worker outer"? Then it becomes challenging to get started? Once you get motivated enough to start exercising, there's the pain of doing it and then the days after... then you stop again. This becomes the one treadmill we actually stay on. Start, quit. Start, quit. If we just stopped quitting, we'd never have to start over!

Here's the thing about exercise, or pretty much anything in life, especially health. It's not something we should sit around and think about or even pray about. It's something you should do without pondering over it. Back to our mindset for a moment; start thinking that you're a healthy person, and you do what healthy people do. One of those things is to work out regularly. Even if you aren't working out today, in your mind, tell yourself that you do exercise! Tell yourself you don't miss workouts; you work out regularly! If you're already someone who works out, great; keep going. If you don't work out at all or know you should become more active, then this next section is for you. God makes it simple to get started with your physical health, and best of all, you can see the results with just a little bit of effort. Remember, you're just going to work with how God created you. You work smarter, not necessarily harder. The purest forms of exercise that will get you the most bang for your time are the ones that you can do at whatever age and fitness level you are. The most important thing to understand about exercise is that anything is better than nothing. But I like to focus on functional exercises or exercises that help your ability to do life better, things that your child and an older person can do without getting hurt. It's fun and exciting to lift heavy weights and to run a far distance, and to have big biceps and chiseled abs, but it's not necessary for you to do day-to-day things or to even be living well. If you could be functionally fit, with only minutes of exercise per week, would that make working out easier? You won't need to go to the gym or have a lot of equipment, although it helps to have some things. If you do the math, that's minutes per week without the cost and time of going to the gym. Doing functional exercises in a specific way may elicit better results than more time and more money spent. I think this becomes a God thing. He made us to be healthy and active, so if we can just tap into those resources, we'll see God-given results, no matter what your activity level is.

If you're a beginner, all the exercises and workouts you'll be doing are without any additional weights, other than your body weight. As you get stronger and more able, you'll slowly add in more weights and more advanced movements.

Here's a list of basic exercises that can be adapted to almost everyone and all fitness levels. Even my four-year-old does these with me. Now, as you gain more understanding of what you're capable of doing, we can create workouts or groups of exercises done at certain times and durations with varying degrees of intensity. Here's just the beginning of what you can be doing at home. I've focused on the more functionally fit exercises with little to no need for specific equipment.

Squats

Lunges

Push-Ups

Sit-Ups

Crunches

Plank

Side Planks

Reverse Crunches

Good Mornings

Superman

Mountain Climbers

Burpees

Frog Squats

Step-Ups

Shoulder Press

Thrusters

Walking/Speed Walking

These are just to get you started. When we develop workouts to do, you will first pick and choose the exercises you enjoy doing and then go from there. The point of these workouts is again to maximize your body's ability to burn fat, increase oxygen to your cells, and, thereby, increase your performance in life. If you're only going to be working out a few minutes per week, you need to work hard in those few minutes.

You want to aim to get your heart rate between 70-90% of its max. You can calculate by subtracting (220-Your Age) then multiplying that by 70-90%.

For example, if you are 40, your max heart rate is (220-40)*.8=144. So, your goal during exercise is to get your heart rate to 144 beats in a minute. Or, you can divide 144 by six, and in a 10 second period, your heart rate should be 24.

If you're thinking about getting your heart rate up to 70-90% of its max, you may be a little freaked out; it does seem a little scary. Here's the thing about exercise, and exercising for benefits you may have never seen before, you have to get comfortable with being uncomfortable. Remember: God gave you a spirit of victory, of overcoming, of Abundance! Everything that you want in terms of your health exists on the other side of being comfortable. Back to your mindset! You may be thinking that you hate to work out, that you'd, instead, do anything else. I'll repeat it; you're not working out for you! You're doing it to honor God with your body and for those people who care about you and whom you're living for. If we were to do things only for ourselves, we wouldn't do anything worthwhile! Always, always, always be anchored to something greater than yourself. Before every workout, before you go to the grocery store, be anchored to your why.

Again, you just have to get started. There's never going to be the right time when you feel like it. You just have to get going. If you need help, some people can help you. I'm here to help you. Call me! Email me! You're not in this alone. Find an accountability partner. Get healthier together. Get your church to workout with you. Get your place of work moving!

So, what does an actual workout look like? If our goal is to get to a higher heart rate, we need to move in a higher intensity for a short period of time. If you're going to get serious results in a few minutes a week, you're going to have to kick it up a notch!

Here are a few sample workouts to get you started:

Do each exercise for 20 seconds as fast as YOU can. Then Rest for 10 seconds. Repeat three times. Then Rest for 1 minute and move onto the next exercise.

- Squats
- Push-Ups
- Lunges
- Bonus Round of 1 Minute: Sit-Ups

Set a timer to count up. Complete the following within a 1-minute timeframe. Rest the remainder of the minute. Then repeat five times.

- 5 Squats
- 5 Push-Ups
- 10 Mountain Climbers
- Bonus Round of 1 minute: Plank

These workouts should be done to your max. They are quick but effective IF you do them correctly. After each, you should feel like your heart is pounding! Everyone is different, and you will reach your heart rate goal at different times. If you're out of shape, then doing only part of the workout will likely get you to your 70% of max. If you're in better shape, you'll need to go faster and longer to get to that max. The benefits of this type of exercise are astronomical! Just to name a few of the benefits, you'll burn more calories in a short time. You'll most likely stick to it. You won't get bored as quickly. You'll improve endurance better than long-duration cardio. You'll burn more fat for longer after your workout. This type of exercise improves heart function and increases oxygen intake. It's easier on your joints. You'll gain muscle and lower blood sugar and blood pressure. You'll improve your metabolic function for hours after your workout! But you need to work!

You are worth it! It's not always a pleasant journey, but it's always worth it. Just get started! We're here if you need help! And better yet, cling to God. He is the one who will always be a part of you and with you. He will give you the strength and encouragement to keep going!Deuteronomy 31:6, "Be strong and courageous. Do not be afraid or terrified because of them; for the Lord, your God goes with you; he will never leave you or forsake you." Philippians 4:13, "I can do all things through him who gives me strength."

2 Timothy 4:7, "I have fought the good fight, I have finished the race, I have kept the faith."Fuel your Body!

1 Corinthians 6:19-20, "Or do you not know that your body is a temple of the Holy Spirit within you, whom you have from God? You are not your own, for you were bought with a price. So glorify God in your body."

1 Corinthians 10:31, "So, whether you eat or drink, or whatever you do, do all to the glory of God."

Genesis 1:29, "And God said, "Behold, I have given you every plant yielding seed that is on the face of all the earth, and every tree with seed in its fruit. You shall have them for food." Action Step 3: This may be the most dreaded aspect of our healthcare: food. Not necessarily the eating of it, but what will give your body the necessary fuel so that it will function at a high level. This section could easily be over a few hundred pages, but I'll keep it simple. Why? I think health is simple; we just overcomplicate it. Let's start with the mindset of food. We all know that eating healthy is critical to fueling our body and promoting health. But bad eating habits can be one of the quickest ways to have our health deteriorate. Eating is something we do every day, and it can become out of hand in a short time. I've seen dozens of documentaries about food. People eat terrible food for 30 days, and we see their overall health deteriorate so rapidly that they develop diseases of their organs. They gain weight, become diabetic or pre-diabetic, develop liver diseases and hypertension, get depressed and lose their zest for life, start needing medications; the list goes on. I've also seen films in which people completely change their diet and, in a matter of days and weeks, completely reverse health issues like those I just mentioned. So, I think you know that what you put into your body does matter. Food does make an impact on how your body is working! So, fuel it with food that will cause high performance. Again, what is your why in this situation? Eating becomes one of the most challenging aspects of our health, but it doesn't have to be. If you're living a life that's only yours, then it doesn't matter what you eat; you'll put things into your body that build sickness. If you're living for God and your family, then it becomes much more important to fuel your body with good food, and it's much easier to be successful.

Nutrition is one of the most discussed areas of our health. I hear of diets every other week that promise to do this or that. You see ads for pills to help you lose weight and lose your appetite or surgeries to shrink your stomach, so you lose weight. You can find pretty much anything online and get sold into doing it. What I'll cover over this section is a food plan you can take with you for the rest of your life, and, best of all, it's simple, and it works! It works to help with weight loss; it helps to make you feel better; and it helps to allow your body to start working for you and not against you. It's a plan established by God. The best part, I think you already know most of it.

I will say that a few "diets" are great, and I would recommend them to specific people, depending on their current situation. However, for most people, living a day-to-day life, the following will help you significantly. As we get through some of the nuts and bolts of nutrition, I'll highlight some different plans of eating that do fit well into our basic plan. That becomes important for those who need to lose a lot of weight or need help healing and reversing a diagnosis. The real key with a God-focused healthcare plan isn't to do it for a few days or a few weeks, but to adopt a lifestyle for God. If something doesn't seem to be "working" right away, know that it is; you may not see it or feel it. Keep living this lifestyle for a month, six months, a year, ten years, then see how you are. But just get started as soon as possible.

One last thing I need to vent about is doctor's attitude toward nutrition. Have you ever been to a doctor or have a family member visit their doctor, and the doctor says, "It doesn't matter what you eat; eat whatever you want. It doesn't affect your outcomes"? Many of my patients tell me this, and I feel like driving to their doctor's office and screaming at them! Are you kidding me? You have diabetes, you have cancer, and it doesn't matter what you put into your body?! It's insane! It's borderline malpractice! If they're good doctors and they say something like, "Of course, it's important what you eat, but I'm not exactly sure what you need" that's an excellent place to start. Most doctors don't focus on health; they focus on the treatment, and treatment typically assumes drugs and surgery. They aren't healthcare providers; they're sick care providers. There's a difference. Anchor to a God-focused healthcare plan, and you won't need a sick care provider.

Where do we begin? Vegetables are good. Processed cookies and treats are bad. With me so far? Of course, we know what's good and what's bad. But a lot of information out there is conflicting and can be detrimental to our health. We'll also look at the Bible for guidance. The goal of our nutrition plan is to keep it simple yet sustainable. Yes, everyone is different and has different needs, but if you just put into place this nutrition plan, it will take you far. And if needed, we can tweak it to tailor our personal needs.

Let's start with some basics. Proteins. Carbohydrates. Fats. You've heard of all of these. Remember, we're eating to live and not living to eat; there's a big difference. When we switch our mindset to eating and living for God, then we can change our behavior to best suit our bodies and how they operate. We want to fuel it for high performance and long-distance traveling, not a short term to just get you there and survive. The body's best source of energy is fat. Your body prefers to burn fat for its primary source of fuel. This is a great thing for most of us! Yes, you can eat fat! But good fats.

Fat will give you nine calories of energy per gram. Carbohydrates, on the other hand, will only give you four calories of energy per gram. So, you'll have to eat double the amount of carbs to make up the energy one gram of healthy fat can give you. Proteins also will provide four calories per gram. Your body is efficient. It wants to work smarter, not harder. We just don't allow it to work. We are continually having to have our body adapt and survive, versus healing and thriving. No wonder we have so much chronic disease!

So now that we know fat is a significant energy source, we need to start adding in healthy amounts of good quality fat. Fat isn't our enemy! When the low-fat movement came into play and fat was removed from our foods, sugar (a carbohydrate) was added to take its place. Since then, we have seen a steady rise in chronic illnesses like heart disease, cancer, diabetes, obesity, and Alzheimer's. Coincidence? I don't think so. We've removed an essential nutrient from our lives, made it an enemy, and replaced it with a processed, anti-nutrient: SUGAR! Fat became our most significant missing nutrient! Here's the thing about fat. It makes up most of our cells. It's crucial to our survival. Fats line our cells to allow for proper detoxification, helps absorb vitamins, hormone production, makes up nearly three-quarters of brain tissue, and your brain runs on fat! Fat enables you to burn fat for energy (we could all use that) and helps reduce inflammation, which is a significant factor in almost all diseases.

Fat is necessary. Sugar and high amounts of carbohydrates are not. More on proteins later (also required). We have had a major over-carbohydrate problem in our society. When you think about carbohydrates, think sugar, they're pretty much the same. Carbohydrates are broken down into glucose or sugar; carbs=sugar=inflammation. Sugars, mainly processed sugars, are the enemy. God never intended for us to ingest so much sugar. It truly is in practically everything these days, from pasta sauces, cookies, crackers, salad dressings, sodas, breads, yogurt, juice, and energy drinks. It's insane! "Everything in moderation!" Good luck, moderating sugar! If you truly wanted to moderate sugar, you have to avoid it at all costs, and then you can reduce it. Sugar is in that many things. It's even naturally in fruit! Am I saying not to eat fruit? Yes. Most fruit. Until you have corrected whatever health concerns you have, fruit is a food by God, but again, He never intended us to be consuming the amounts of sugars we have been. The key to fats is to fix the fats you're already eating and to replace the fats that are causing us harm. Yup, there are bad fats that you NEED to avoid as you would sugar. We don't want to make a God-given fat dangerous. Add the good fats and eliminate the bad fats. Here is a list of bad fats to avoid and good fats to incorporate into your day.

Bad fats:

- Hydrogenated and Partially Hydrogenated Oils: cottonseed oil, soybean oil, vegetable oils.
- Trans Fats: margarine and synthetic butter.
- "Corn oil," canola oil, or those labeled vegetable oils.

Good fats (not altered by man):

- Extra virgin olive oil
- Avocados and avocado oil
- Coconut and coconut oil
- Raw Nuts, seeds, and oils
- Real butter (raw is best)
- Raw cheese and yogurt
- Grass-fed: meats, eggs, whole milk
- Fatty fish: Pacific or Wild salmon, small fish, sardines

When it comes to fats, you can make an excellent fat dangerous when you heat it. So, good fats to cook with are Avocado oil or coconut oil. All the oils listed under bad fats, avoid them like the plague! Bad fats can cause a host of issues and lead to inflammation and damaged cells.

Sugars and Bad Fats=DISEASE. It's that simple.

Food Rule #1: Add in healthier fats. Remove, eliminate bad, damaged fats.

Food Rule #2: Avoid sugars in all their forms: Processed foods, cookies, crackers, sauces, dressings, sodas, diet sodas, Artificial Sweeteners (worse than just sugar), most fruit.

Food Rule #3: Perfect your Proteins: When it comes to protein, we typically just think of meat. Meat can be great for you; it can also be dangerous for you. What? Let's keep it simple. When it comes to all foods, what once was good and healthy has now been ruined by man (a product of this broken world).

If man has touched it, it has been tampered with; it's now a version of what God has given to us. We now have a culture that's all about making more and more. With that comes big money! The meat we consume is from animals that have been fed grains, corn, and hormones to make them bigger, faster. They're unhealthy animals, fish included.

We must be careful of the proteins we eat. Be cautious about "other" forms of protein if you're a vegan or vegetarian, specifically soy. Soy can alter hormones and cause a host of problems. If you're vegan or vegetarian, stick with plant-based proteins that are not modified. Plants contain the building blocks of proteins that will give you what you need. At a minimum, I suggest a high-quality plant protein powder.

Quality Fats to Add: Avocados, Pasture Raised Eggs, Raw nuts and seeds, coconut oil, olive oil, avocado oil, Raw butter, Raw cheese and yogurts, Grass-fed meats, flaxseed, ghee.

Quality Carbohydrates to Add: Asparagus, cauliflower, broccoli, spinach, zucchini, celery, green beans, kale, peppers, mushrooms, cabbage, spaghetti squash.

Quality Proteins to Add: Grass-fed beef, venison, free-range chicken, wild-caught fish, natural or raw dairy. Plant protein powder (except soy) for those who are vegan or vegetarian.

Alternative Sweeteners to Add as necessary: Xylitol, stevia, monk fruit, honey (in minimal doses)

Genesis 1:30, "And to every beast of the earth and every bird of the heavens and to everything that creeps on the earth, everything that has the breath of life, I have given every green plant for food." And it was so.

Genesis 9:3, "Every moving thing that lives shall be food for you. And as I gave you the green plants, I give you everything."

Proverbs 25:27, "It is not good to eat much honey, nor is it glorious to seek one's own glory."

Remember: this healthcare system is about taking it with you for the rest of your life. If you're having a health crisis or a need to improve your health quickly, we may alter what you're doing, but this will get you started toward better health. I love that even in the Bible, God says to eat meat (in the way He designed it), to eat vegetables, greens, and to stay away from sugar (honey)! Even in the Proverbs verse about not overeating honey, you shouldn't seek your own glory! As if seeking one's own glory is just as bad as overeating honey! I think God put swarms of bees around honey (even though it's natural) to protect us from eating it too readily. When it comes to food, ask yourself if it's something God would want you to eat, and think about how it came to be. You shouldn't be eating pounds of sugar. Why? It's way too difficult to gather in nature. We just made it so easy to get. We have now overproduced it to make it too easy to eat.

Proverbs 23:20-21, "Be not among drunkards or gluttonous eaters of meat, for the drunkard and the glutton will come to poverty, and slumber will clothe them with rags."

Philippians 3:19, "Their end is destruction, their god is their belly, and they glory in their shame, with minds set on earthly things."Meats or proteins are a necessary aspect of our food intake. God says that we may eat meat, but not in an overabundance. Too much protein can cause health issues, especially if it's not of good quality. This is why you need to begin getting better quality meats. Look for "wild-caught" "grass-fed" or "free-range" meats and eggs. If you're going to eat meat, make sure it's the best quality. One meat the Bible says to avoid, can you name it?Deuteronomy 14:8, "And the pig, because it parts the hoof but does not chew the cud, is unclean for you. Their flesh you shall not eat, and their carcasses you shall not touch."

Leviticus 11:4-14, "Nevertheless, among those that chew the cud or part the hoof, you shall not eat these: The camel, because it chews the cud but does not part the hoof, is unclean to you. And the rock badger, because it chews the cud but does not part the hoof, is unclean to you. And the hare, because it chews the cud but does not part the hoof, is unclean to you. And the pig, because it parts the hoof and is cloven-footed but does not chew the cud, is unclean to you. "You shall not eat any of their flesh, and you shall not touch their carcasses; they are unclean to you." When we listen to the Bible as to what it says on eating, we gain a host of knowledge. Many of these animals described are toxic, and, therefore, you wouldn't want to eat them. The real issue then becomes the processing of these animals, pigs especially. I'm not sure if anyone is eating camels or badgers. When humans process this meat and add preservatives, it becomes even more toxic and dangerous to our health. These processed foods and meats are linked to cancer! If you eat meat, just eat it as it was intended. It does become one of the most important food groups to eat as naturally as you can find it! Why? It is one of the most processed foods we see. When these animals are born and raised in a conventional setting, they're given hormones and medications to keep them from becoming ill, while also growing them bigger faster and typically in an inhumane environment. Find grass-fed cows, pasture-raised chickens, and wild-caught fish. Don't overcomplicate it, but when it comes to meat, you need to get quality, God-made meats. Here's a quick aside on fruits. This is a topic that comes up a lot when we start to alter our diet. God made fruit. Fruit can be loaded with sugars. When you're trying to get your health back and build it back up, you must avoid most fruits. Why? Sugar. Sugar is sugar. Do not over consume these foods because you don't want to throw the body out of a fat-burning mode and set it back into burning sugar. So, most fruits are best to avoid. Berries, lemons, limes, granny smith apples are best to eat in moderation. Moderation means a few times per week. The same goes for vegetables. Those that can spike blood sugar are typically the ones grown underground, potatoes, onions, carrots. Keep with the above-ground vegetables. Even when people do the Daniel Fast (it's in the Bible), they tend to overconsume fruits and do not eat enough vegetables. Again, do not take something that you can eat and overconsume it.

Daniel 1:8-20, "But Daniel resolved that he would not defile himself with the king's food or with the wine that he drank. Therefore he asked the chief of the eunuchs to allow him not to defile himself. And God gave Daniel favor and compassion in the sight of the chief of the eunuchs, and the chief of the eunuchs said to Daniel, "I fear my lord the king, who assigned your food and your drink; for why should he see that you were in worse condition than the youths who are of your own age? So you would endanger my head with the king." Then Daniel said to the steward whom the chief of the eunuchs had assigned over Daniel, Hananiah, Mishael, and Azariah, "Test your servants for ten days; let us be given vegetables to eat and water to drink."Fasting:

"I ate no choice food; no meat or wine touched my lips, and I used no lotions at all until the three weeks were over." Daniel 10:3

"So we fasted and petitioned our God about this, and he answered our prayer." Ezra 8:23

Many times, throughout the Bible, fasting is used as a way to get closer to God. There is now even more research showing the health benefits of fasting. This may be a tool that can be used to help not only get you closer to your health goals but also to rely and lean on God more in many aspects of your life. It's a win-win. Some benefits of fasting include: increased sensitivity to insulin (helpful if you have diabetes), increased weight loss, boosted metabolism, improves brain function, strengthened immune system, helps to repair damaged tissues throughout your body, may help in promoting longevity, helps burn fat, reduces inflammation, helps heal the digestive system, and the list goes on.

Fasting can be a scary thought for many of us. "Not eating?" To experience the benefits of fasting, you don't have to go without food for weeks and months; I would advise against that. However, you can simply implement certain types of fasting into your day or week without changing your lifestyle all that much.

Begin with a quick and easy fast; stop eating for 12-14 hours. This helps take stress off the digestive system and helps begin transitioning your body to burning fat.

The fasting duration can increase from there. You can choose to fast 16-18 hours, one to three times per week. I will typically fast for 18-24 hours two to three times per month. Saturday or Sunday is a great time to begin a fast. Sunday is a day of rest. Rest your digestive system and allow healing to occur. This will continue with the previous benefits of fasting as well as improving and helping to reverse chronic disease. This is something to aim for if you need to shift your health in a big way. Doing this a few days per week and adding in our nutrition plan from above will no doubt give you the best opportunity to rebuild your health.

Fasting can be a significant method of helping your body heal. Get in touch with a healthcare provider, or reach out to us, to help get you started. When done correctly, you can see massive benefits in a short time. Depending on your needs, fasting can be done in a variety of ways, changing times and what you do and do not eat. Implement fasting a few days per week, or throughout the month. This is something that will get easier as you do it more often. The benefits will be dramatic and long-lasting. Again, when fasting, know why you're doing it and anchor to God.

The bread question:

So, I can't have bread anymore?! Simply put, "No." But if you want bread, and yes, I do too, get something that's from the Bible! If you haven't found it yet, it's called Ezekiel bread.

Ezekiel 4:9, "And you, take wheat and barley, beans and lentils, millet and emmer, and put them into a single vessel and make your bread from them. During the number of days that you lie on your side, 390 days, you shall eat it."

Even with this, although it's "approved," consume it irregularly throughout the week, 1-3 times, and try only having it in the morning. The same goes for the healthy types of grains, millet, quinoa, lentils, etc. These should all be consumed in strict moderation. Again, we're working our way toward our God-given health potential, and we need to be rigid. Removing a lot of unhealthy foods, although they may seem healthy, is a necessary part of regaining our health. We weren't designed to get sick and build disease, so we need to do things differently so we can reverse what we have developed.

I will say there are some alternatives that you can add to your diet to replace the wheat and bread in your diet. Use flax meal, almond meal, cashew meal, coconut flour, and other nut flours. There are countless recipes you can find that will replace typical recipes and replace them with these healthier alternatives.

We have become a society built on bread. Everything is focused around bread or wheat products. We eat sandwiches, pasta dinners, breakfasts with bagels, toast, pancakes, and waffles, then loaded with syrup and dressings and artificial butter. It's insane how much bread we consume. Bread is not necessary to survive. One type of bread is necessary but cannot be made or bought, and I will end nutrition with that. It is the bread of life. Not the bread of this earth.

John 6:51, "I am the living bread that came down from heaven. If anyone eats of this bread, he will live forever. And the bread that I will give for the life of the world is my flesh."

The Alcohol Question
I often get asked about alcohol and if it's OK to consume it if you're trying to get healthy. It can be a complicated and straightforward answer, but mostly simple. The answer is "No," it's not OK to drink alcohol; it's not a health food. It's a toxin. Your body has to stop what it's doing and focus its energy on removing the alcohol. This is the same idea when it comes to anything that isn't healthy that we put into our bodies. We have to shift our body's focus away from healing and repair and refocus it onto detoxing and surviving, so the simple answer is, "No."

Get your power on!

Action Step 4: Refer to Chapter 5. Find a good doctor of chiropractic who is well-versed in the principles of health. If at first, you don't succeed, find someone else. This is a crucial part of your overall health. Your nervous system needs to be checked and corrected as necessary. Make it a family affair. Connect your brain to your body. Just the way God intended for it to be.

SUMMARY-TAKE 5

- Protect your mindset. Anchor to God. If you win your mindset, you will succeed. Keep anchored to your "why." Get some tan lines!
- Get physical! Get used to being uncomfortable. Your body is made to move, so get moving!
- Give your body quality food! Remove the bad fats, oils, and sugars. Eat to live and stop living to eat. Seek help if needed.
- Get your nervous system checked and adjusted regularly. The more aspects of building your health you add to your life, the better, and faster your positive outcomes occur. Do not wait. Make the jump!
- Health is an action. You must pursue health. Health does not just come to you. Take action with God's principles of health. Make them a part of who you are.

CHAPTER 10

THE TEST

Do not give the devil a foothold.

Ephesians 4:27

The thief comes only to steal, kill and destroy. I have come that they may have life and life to the fullest.

John 10:10

This is a difficult chapter to write. Why? When you or I set out to do something greater than ourselves, to do something God-focused, something that will have a lasting purpose, there will always be a test. Always. What kind of test? It will come in many ways and forms. The devil is as real as God is. The devil wants you to fail. It's as simple as that. For you to fully experience God's abundance in your health, there needs to be a test so that you may overcome what this world has allowed to happen, and so that God can be the healer.

When it comes to stepping toward health, which is one of your most valuable assets, be prepared for something or someone to step in your way. It will always happen. If life is going too easy and there aren't many things you're concerned about, then you're most likely running with the devil. When things are being thrown at you and life is getting crazy, you're confused about everything you're trying to do, and life seems to be unraveling around you, then you're most likely running against the devil and into God's place for you. The same will be true with your health.

I find it to be true that the devil doesn't necessarily need our lives to be entirely destroyed for him to have victory over us. He merely needs us to live in a constant state of mediocrity. He wants us to believe that we're doing just OK. This is the ultimate killer and life destroyer, just being OK, mediocre. This is a state of survival. The problem lies in the fact that if we continue to do the same things or a lack of the same things over time, we don't stay the same; we're on a slow trajectory pointed down toward more sickness, disease, and pain, not necessarily quickly, just continuously. As Christ-followers, we need to be able to see this is happening and to quickly navigate away from this state of mediocrity and move into a state of God's greatness.

When I begin to work with someone, they finally are ready for a lasting change. They're tired of being sick and tired. Almost always, within a matter of days, they have some sort of an excuse. "I can't eat well this weekend; it's my birthday! I have to go to a wedding. How am I supposed to stick to my plan? I'm on vacation next week. We're visiting friends tomorrow night, and they don't eat well." The list goes on and on. When it comes to your nutrition plan, and when you decide to choose healthier eating habits, there will always be something that comes flying in to take you down. They'll recall lettuce, or there won't be the right kind of almond or flax meal to cook with, you'll buy the wrong sweetener, you'll get tired and just order pizza, or your spouse will say, "Are you serious about doing this?" All of these are only little nicks that the devil is throwing at you to tell you to stop already and go back to your nice, semi-comfortable life. I find it especially true when we're working on getting healthier. It's an easy target for the enemy. When you don't have your full health and full life potential, you're not experiencing and showing God's full love and expression. It's just not possible.

The next test is right after you want to begin the exercise component of your health. This isn't an option, by the way; it's essential. It's necessary. So, we start slowly; we begin on purpose on what we do and how we do it. Within days, someone will sprain their ankle walking to work, slip and fall on some ice, trip on some stairs and hurt their knee, be too sore to work out the next day, pull a muscle, or just mentally give up. It happens all the time! These are all just tests to get us to stop becoming greater. To hold us, and keep us in a state of, just OK. When we're in this pattern, we're not just staying the same. There's no such thing as the same. We're either getting stronger or weaker, closer to a fuller life or closer to a shorter life. Where do you think the enemy wants you? Working out and exercising is often on people's to-do list. It's never really something most of us get around to doing.

My wife is one of the most organized people I know, and she gets stuff done! She constantly has notebooks out and lists of things to do, mostly life stuff: food shopping, buy this for school, call an electrician, laundry. As I'm writing this now, she's crossing things off the list and writing other things to do. This list is for both of us. My point is, every day, on her to-do list, she has "workout." It has become a part of who she is, of who we are. It's not an "if I get around to it" item; it needs to get done, just like anything else needs to get done. If she misses a workout one day, guess what the first thing is on the list the next day? Workout. Why? It's a priority. We don't get the luxury of just forgetting about our health, putting it off, or even ignore it. It's not OK. Yes, at times, a lot is happening and working out or working out how we want to is just not going to happen. But something gets done; even a three- to five-minute workout gets done. Why only a few minutes? It's effective, but also, it keeps us on track, it keeps us from going too far off the path.

I've been working with a patient for a few years. Like most, she does well when she puts in the time and effort. When she doesn't, her knees bother her. Her hips are painful, she gets headaches and numbness in her hands, and it's pretty clear to see when she gets off the plan and allows life to interfere with her health. But, when she does get back on track, starts eating God's way, and starts to workout, guess what I see and hear? I see a happier version of her, a less complaining version, and I hear more positivity and laughter. We have been working out in my office for the last few weeks, and she just shows up. When I say you don't need to be great to get started or to be a superstar when you're working out, I mean it. She's not moving fast; she is not doing any explosive movements; she just shows up and does what she can. And guess what? She gets a good workout in, she comes in the next day and has sore muscles, but different sore from her usual pains. If you have ever started a workout plan, the first days are the WORST! You feel like your legs are going to fail you while walking downstairs. You think you may never stand up from the toilet, you'll be stranded in the bathroom all day, or you'll have to take time from work because you can't move. It's a great feeling. Get used to this feeling. Long for this feeling. Welcome this feeling. This is the pain of growth. This is the pain of moving forward. We must get comfortable with feeling uncomfortable, especially when it comes to the exercise aspect of health. Become someone who longs for that soreness of a great workout. Disregard the enemy. Work out when you sprain your ankle or get a blister; just do something that doesn't involve that part of your body. Quit using excuses the devil is giving you. See it for what it is, a test, a foothold. Don't allow him to use your weaknesses against you.

Revelation 3:15 says, "I know your deeds, that you are neither cold nor hot. I wish you were either one or the other. So because you are lukewarm, I am about to spit you out of my mouth."

In this Bible verse, we see that being on both sides of the fence doesn't get you anywhere, in fact it gets you spit out! I find that many people are lukewarm, kind of hot, kind of cold, not really swaying one way or the other when it comes to many aspects of their life, especially health. This is the devils battle plan. Get us to not want greatness and not be on fire for our lives. He wants us to watch the negative news, take more medication, keep ordering fast food, and continue spending money on things that take us away from our purpose. Even when you start heating up in our life, getting on fire for bigger things, our friends and family aren't necessarily on the same page. Could the devil be using our own family and friends against us? You bet! Be aware of this. It's not always your job to shift them; you can't control others, just what you do. The more on fire you become, the bigger the test. But with the more significant test, comes the greatest of breakthroughs and victories you may ever see!

Many times, a new patient comes to our office for chiropractic care, see their problems on their x-ray, and fully understand why they're going to work to correct their spine and nervous system. Then they tell their friends and family. Guess what happens next? They call or come in and say, "My friend told me not to get adjusted!" Their friends and family start to infiltrate their thinking to pull them away from getting healthy. This is why the renewing of your mind is so crucial in your health. Health is one of those aspects of your life that if the devil can grab a foothold, he has you for as long as you live, just getting by, surviving. He may not take you entirely down today, but it's the idea of death by a thousand cuts. You're allowed to be just OK.

Even along our journeys toward health, we all get hung up somewhere. We cannot be perfect; therefore, health problems arise. Diagnoses get made, medication is prescribed, maybe even surgery. Those things may be necessary. They could be part of your test; understand that and rebuke it! Here's the bottom line, no matter what the circumstance, no matter what the diagnosis, it's ALWAYS RIGHT to get healthy! It's always right to remove damaging foods and drinks from your life. It's always right to begin exercising! It's always right to correct your nervous system (finding the right doctor is vital). It's always right to improve your mindset and get stronger spiritually. At times, patients come in who are already having health issues. We go through the protocols, and they end up calling and saying, "My doctor told me not to see you, and it doesn't matter what I eat!" Infuriating! Again, the devil is working through others to take you out! Remember, it's always right to get healthy. Look back and have these principles of health become a part of you.

To have a breakthrough, a TESTimony, there must be a test. I know that when things seem to be at their worst like you are getting your butt handed to you, you're, without a doubt, in the middle of a test. It may not even be an attack on your physical health; it could be financial, work-related, relationally, it's all a part of it. Know the devil is grasping at straws to find what will affect you the most. The more you anchor to God and His laws and principles, the stronger you become, and the quicker the test.

So, who will be disguised as the devil in your life? Who will almost inadvertently want you to fail? Whatever happens, don't be the "devil" in someone else's life. Don't let the devil infiltrate your mind and allow you to bring someone else down!

In Matthew 4, even the devil tempts Jesus! If you think that he won't try and tempt you, you're mistaken. The devil went after Jesus!

"Then Jesus was led up by the Spirit into the wilderness to be tempted by the devil. And when he had fasted forty days and forty nights, afterward he was hungry. Now when the tempter came to him, he said, 'If You are the Son of God, command that these stones become bread.' But he answered and said, 'It is written, "Man shall not live by bread alone, but by every word that proceeds from the mouth of God."' Then the devil took Him up into the holy city, set Him on the pinnacle of the temple, and said to Him, 'If You are the Son of God, throw

Yourself down. For it is written: "He shall give His angels charge over you," and, "In their hands they shall bear you up, lest you dash your foot against a stone.'" Jesus said to him, 'It is written again, "You shall not tempt the Lord your God.'" Again, the devil took Him up on an exceedingly high mountain, and showed Him all the kingdoms of the world and their glory. And he said to Him, 'All these things I will give You if You will fall down and worship me.' Then Jesus said to him, 'Away with you, Satan! For it is written, "You shall worship the Lord your God, and Him only you shall serve.'" Then the devil left Him, and behold, angels came and ministered to Him."

The devil went after Jesus multiple times. He will undoubtedly go after you, not once or twice, but many times. Be aware of what or whom is tempting you. That's where God comes into play. Always rely on Him. He will fight for you and with you. We must learn to know that we are wavering off course. The better we become at noticing ourselves getting lost, the sooner we can stop and get back on track. Anchor to God. Anchor to His health laws. You will be brought back on course.

The devil is powerful, conniving, and brilliant. But do you know who has NEVER lost a battle? Our God. He is bigger than all the attacks that can be made against you. He is stronger. He is more powerful. He has an army of angels to surround and protect you. He is always fighting for your favor, always! If you've pushed God away, allow Him back in your corner, let Him be your trainer, he's undefeated! That's who I want to work out with. That's who I want to anchor to. Remember, the point of the anchor is to hold you, to keep you. But it doesn't do its job unless there's a storm above the water. Sometimes, we need to feel the storm for our anchor to do its job.

Psalm 25:5, "Guide me in your truth and teach me, for you are my God and Savior, and my hope is in you all day long."

Psalm 61:2, "From the ends of the Earth I call to you, I call as my heart grows faint; lead me to the rock that is higher than I."

SUMMARY-TAKE 5

- Commit to beginning your health journey. Be aware that the obstacles you face are just a test, and a bump for you to stumble over.
- It is always a great time to get healthy. It is always right.
- There will be a test, and it will happen. It's just a matter of when and how big.
- The enemy is coming; be careful whom he may be disguised as.
- Keep your anchor. The storm will happen, your anchor will keep you safe.

CHAPTER 11

RAISING HEALTHY FAMILIES: ESPECIALLY KIDS

Train up a child in the way he should go;
even when he is old, he will not depart from it.

Proverbs 22:6

For you formed my inward parts;
you knitted me together in my mother's womb. I
praise you, for I am fearfully and wonderfully made.
Wonderful are your works; my soul knows it very well.
My frame was not hidden from you when
I was being made in secret, intricately woven
in the depths of the earth. Your eyes saw
my unformed substance; in your book were written,
every one of them, the days that were formed for me,
when as yet there was none of them.

Psalm 139:13-16

Or do you not know that your body is a temple
of the Holy Spirit within you, whom you have from God?

You are not your own, for you were bought with a price.
So, glorify God in your body.

1 Corinthians 6:19-20

If you're a parent, grandparent, aunt, or uncle, you have children in your life; our children's health is an essential and vital subject. Like every other aspect of our lives, I urge you to focus on how God wants us to bring up our children. This isn't about how to raise your children; it's about keeping our children healthy to give them the best opportunity to be and stay well throughout their lives.

According to the *Journal of the American Medical Association* (*JAMA*), 1 in 10 children have asthma, ADHD is the most common neurodevelopmental disorder, Cancer is the LEADING CAUSE of disease DEATH in children, 1 in 6 has a developmental disorder, epilepsy affects 1 in 20 children, 1 in 68 have autism, and Juvenile Diabetes is up 23% in a matter of years. Chronic health conditions for children have increased dramatically in the past four decades and have risen from 12.8% in 1994 to almost 27% in 2007. The most dramatic statistic is that the U.S has one of the highest infant mortality rates in the industrialized world! Nearly 7 babies out of 1,000 will die before their first birthday! These seem like apocalyptic type numbers. In just a matter of years, the health of our children has decreased significantly. If you don't think that this is a big deal, think again! These are chronic health conditions. Chronic disease is defined as longer than a few months that can last for years if not someone's entire life. That means more doctor visits, more medications, more diagnoses, and more money! Tell me if this is what our God intended for our children. I doubt it. If we are to bring more of God into our lives and this world, let it begin with raising healthy children!

We can comfortably sit back and just blame the world for these outcomes. And it's true; this world is sick, diseased, and broken. We can also say it's genetic, and we all know that you cannot have a shift in genetics that causes all these diseases over a short time. So, again, like adult health, it goes back to what we're doing to either build our children's health or to take it away slowly. Raise sick kids, get sick adults, and that cycle continues. Raise healthy children, get healthy adults, and that cycle continues. Which do you prefer? Which would your children prefer? Let's raise our children in the way they should go, and when they are adults, they shall not depart from it.

I've found that as people get excited about their lives and start committing to God's healthcare plans, they sometimes forget about the other people in their lives, their spouse, or, more importantly, their children. So often, a mom or dad will come to see me and tell me that they are doing so great with their adjustments and their food preparation; they may even be down a few pounds, but in the same breath, they'll tell me that they just took their children through a fast-food drive-thru because they were running late. You can imagine the face I would make. They're telling me that they, the parent or adult, who is responsible for their children, would rather eat quality nutrients, workout, get adjusted but then turn around and feed their children junk food that has little to no nutrient value. It gets confusing. If our health is so important and if God's laws about health and healing are true, then they pertain to our entire family, especially our children! We need to collectively be aware and extremely diligent about keeping our kids' health a priority. If we don't, then their chances of being unhealthy adults, who need a prescription medication or surgeries and have chronic health issues, goes up dramatically.

Let's begin to change the generations! If you have kids, go on this health journey with them. How you speak to your children about everything becomes who they are and how they deal with this life. As my son gets older, I can see how his personality changes as well as his behavior. These years are by no means "easy," but, as a parent, you begin to learn that not only what you tell your children but also how you speak to them matters. I'll stick to the matters of health and raising your children with the mindset of health that leads to their actions. I'll confess right off the bat that my son does have the occasional treats. Hershey Kisses are his favorite! Again, these things are not a staple in our house; they are there rarely. But, the same principles of health that affect your life also affect your children's lives. Let's briefly revisit them now and how they pertain to our children.

My son is all boy. He typically has at least one scraped knee, cut or scratch, or something that was recently bleeding, most likely his lip. If he gets hurt, has the typical tearful response you would get from a toddler: "Is it bleeding?!" After we can assess and make sure he's alright, and we're calm, he also calms down. The question I ask him next goes something like this, "Remember, what does our body do?" His response is always, "it heals." The most exciting part of this is after a few days of the scrape on his foot, or wherever it may be that week, starts to get noticeably better, he'll realize it, and, in his high-pitched excitement, say, "Daddy, it healed!" My wife and I will always be reminding him that his body does heal; it's always trying to heal. We just need to let it do its job and not interfere with it. Do your children know that their bodies are designed to heal, that they're capable of healing? Or are they being taught that they need medication or a shot in their arm to keep them healthy? Never has my son asked for a prescription when he's feeling under the weather. Maybe because he has never had a medication, prescribed or over the counter. He also has never had to go to the doctor for a sick visit. This is not about never giving your child medication or avoiding doctors, of course. My son has had symptoms that are not fun to deal with, but we honor his body, and ride it out together. The less interference, the better.

The first step is to start building your child's mindset up about their body and how it heals. Use a cut on their arm from an accident as the first lesson, or even a cut on your arm. Watch it heal together over a few days. Watch them be in awe! Do your children know that their bodies can heal? Do they think they need a drug or medication to cure them? Right now, ask your child, "Who heals you?" What is their response? The sooner in life that they know that God is their healer, not humans or the chemicals that may go into them, the sooner they will be healthier and anchored in truth.

Just like you, your child's brain controls everything. Do they have a spine and nerve system? Does their spine and nerve system control and coordinate all functions in their bodies? Yes! This is why we see children in my practice. It's as simple as that. We might as well keep their body functioning as well as we can at the youngest possible age, or they have to fix it later.

When someone tells me about their child, niece or nephew, or even grandchild who has a health issue, I say, "Bring them in." Let's start correcting or at least checking to see if their spine is interfering with their nerve system. Then, like any adult, we move onto the next thing, which is typically nutrition.

Does it matter what your child eats? I hope you'd say, "Yes." Of course, it does. My son eats what we eat. To be honest, even if my wife and I have a night of a "vacation meal," like pizza or wings and my son will usually have leftovers. He'll have a smoothie we make for him, and then he'll ask for his multivitamin. I think we like to overcomplicate health, especially with our children. My son knows how his body heals and who heals his body. But like every other child, if given a choice between eating broccoli and having a handful of chocolate chips, he'll pick the chocolate chips every time! Let's be more aware and anchored to giving our children the best options we can. We don't need to be perfect; we just need to be moving in the right direction, be on purpose! Stay the course, especially with our children.

If you've had the pleasure of raising tiny humans, you will attest that they are sponges! They know and learn way more than we give them credit for. Over the last few years having our son, we've become more aware of our actions and our words. Our children learn from us. One of the most important lessons I can teach my son, besides being a good human being, is having him understand that God created him in a perfect image that does heal and does get well and let him know the actions that go with that. He not only repeats to me that his body can heal and that God heals him but also sees the efforts that go along with that. He eats the way we eat. He gets the supplements he needs; we take them together. He works out with us in his unique style, but he works out. Afterward, he'll be out of breath and say, "Daddy! We gotta get a recovery shake!" Raising children is already hard enough; being healthy and having them know about their health should only make this job a little easier. Especially if you're anchoring to God's healthcare plan, give them food by God. Let them run around in exercise. Take care of their spines and nerve systems. Invest the time to create positive mindsets about healing. Raise them in the way they should go. When they are older, they will not part from it; they'll be anchored, steadfast.

The value of our health is so crucially important, especially our children's, that we can't afford to take it for granted. Why do we need to run into a crisis before we start realizing this? It's so frustrating, not only as a parent but also a doctor, to see children get sicker and sicker over the years. They're in and out of crisis, and their parents continually do the same things repeatedly. And you can't blame the parents; they just do what they think is best. We all do. Yes, it's in part due to our poor healthcare system, but we'll pray on Sunday for health and healing and know how great God is, but then on Monday, we lose sight of that. Let's raise our children on fire for God, but let them also know that their help, their health also comes from Him!

Matthew 7:13-14, "Enter through the narrow gate. For wide is the gate and broad is the road that leads to destruction, and many enter through it. But small is the gate and narrow the road that leads to life, and only a few find it."

SUMMARY-TAKE 5

- Raise your children in the way they ought to go, even in their health.
- Be on a mission with your children to become healthier. Let's change the health of the next generation of children.
- The same principles of health and healing apply to you as they do for your children.
- Teach your children that God is their healer. Plant the anchor now. It will only get stronger.
- Help raise a generation on fire for God. Let them be healthy. Lead them through the narrow gate to a life with abundance.

CHAPTER 12:

AFTERTHOUGHTS

*For God gave us a spirit not of fear but
of power and love and self-control.*

2 Timothy 1:7

Casting all your anxieties on him, because he cares for you.

1 Peter 5:7

*Whoever walks with the wise becomes wise, but the
companion of fools will suffer harm.*

Proverbs 13:20

*And God is able to make all grace abound to you so that
having all sufficiency in all things at all times;
you may abound in every good work.*

2 Corinthians 9:28

I feel that we have gone through a lot of information that can be overwhelming, and I hope, a little uncomfortable. This book isn't meant to give you all the warm and fuzzy feelings that other books may give you. It's supposed to be a call to action, a "no more excuses" book. There needs to come a time when we all draw a line in the sand and decide to leave the comfortable life behind and begin creating new territory. I find this especially important and challenging in terms of our health. There cannot be another day, week, or year that we allow our health to be forgotten. We don't have the time to let our health decline. God doesn't want you to be sick, tired, broken, or gone too soon. It's time to plant your anchors, "burn the ships," and move to a better quality of health that you've never experienced before. Get on fire for your life!

Since writing this book, my conviction for health has only become more profound. My anchors have only dug deeper. With that, there have been tests, painful, uncomfortable tests! Some of them I've personally put on myself to grow stronger in my faith and health. Others happened without foreseeing. Not all tests are bad. My wife and I will be having another baby soon! This leads us to seek more health and more faith in our lives. We welcome those sorts of tests and growth. God is trusting us with the life of another child.

Other tests come with more of a smack in the face. During this process, my mom suffered a severe health crisis. As with most medical emergencies, this came on quickly. We were living our lives just like I've discussed throughout this book. It happened to us. She was recently at her primary care doctor, and there was nothing to be concerned over. We all assumed she was in excellent health or, at least, what appeared to be good health. She was active and able to get up and down for a nearly seventy-year-old. She took no medication. She looked the part of health. My mom has been, and still is my biggest supporter. She has shown me what faith is and how to live and love. She has taught me perseverance and what it means to be a Christ-follower. My mom has taught me so much.

As time went on and she became more stable, we began to adjust to what had happened. My mom is strong. Her faithfulness never wavered. Her heart never changed. She dug in and is now fighting every day to heal and improve. With four children of her own, and six grandchildren, her 'why' has become even stronger. She has always been the anchor in our family, our strength. She is always putting others before herself. I'm sure we all have someone in our family like that, perhaps it's you. We cannot put our health below everything else. We need my mom. Her children and grandchildren need her. My dad needs her. We cannot afford to wait to get healthy; our health is our most valued asset. Everything hinges on our health. As I've said a hundred times in this book, we cannot assume we're healthy. We need to be in hot pursuit of health and life! We cannot afford the luxury of waiting and hoping that we'll be healthy. We need to take action! It becomes especially true as we get older. If we want to maintain the same level of health and ability as we age, we need to be taking more action, not less!

I've been speaking on health for almost a decade, and my family has heard it before. Very rarely will anyone disagree with me because it is all based on principle, on laws. But we're still human. We choose to go with what this world says, and it often brings us to a crisis. This world affects my family too. If I break the laws of health, I get sick. If I'm not working on improving my health, I also will end up in a crisis.

With my mom, we can easily ask how did this happen and why. These things happen when we break the laws of health. Remember, we're either building health or building disease, and our actions over time tell our results. We can look back and see that, although my mom was never really being destructive with her health, she wasn't necessarily doing anything to bring abundant health to her body. She was eating whatever she wanted, she never really exercised, except for the occasional gardening, she didn't get her nervous system adjusted, and she had a fair amount of stress over the last few years. See, when we allow the pattern of this world to happen to us, our health takes a significant hit. It's not about if; it's about when. When we allow our mindset of being OK to drive our lives, we, sooner or later, end up in a crisis.

Thankfully, my mom is alive and healing. We still have more questions than answers about what caused the problem, but the answer I give is, in the meantime, get healthy! She needs medication right now. She needs doctors right now. But in the time between, we work on building up her mind, her body, and her physical and spiritual health. It's the only thing we can control.

My purpose for what I do, as with many doctors like myself, is to prevent children and grandchildren from losing their parents or grandparents too early, to keep parents from having to bring their children to lifelong treatments to save their lives, so that people can continue to experience quality time, vacations, and laughter with their friends and family. I'm tired of people crying about losing their loved ones way too early! Enough is enough! Let living and living with abundance be a blessing to others. You are here for a purpose; serve it!

Let's anchor to God's healthcare plan and reap the benefits of living a life according to how He created us. Live a life of abundance through Him and for Him.

And do not be conformed to this world, but be transformed by the renewing of your mind, that you may prove what that good and acceptable and perfect will of God is.

Romans 12:2

I have come so that they may have life and have it more abundantly.

John 10:10

Your word is a lamp to my feet and a light to my path.

Psalm 119:105

Submit yourselves therefore to God. Resist the devil, and he will flee from you.

James 4:7

Now Go! Be strong and courageous, do not be afraid or tremble at them, for the LORD your God is the one who goes with you. He will not fail you or forsake you.

Deuteronomy 31:6

TRUSTED DOCTORS

Below, you will find a list of doctors that have been hand-chosen as a quality healthcare partner. They will be able to help guide you and lead you closer to God's abundant health. If there is not a doctor close to you, reach out to one of them, they may be able to help find you someone closer.

CALIFORNIA
Dr. T.J. Osborne
Discover Chiropractic
1305 North Bascom Ave, Ste. C
San Jose, CA 95128
408-985-1111

COLORADO
Dr. Kevin Noffsinger
New Hope Family Wellness
15236 E. Hampden Ave.
Aurora, CO 80014
303-751-5255 x11

Dr. Marcus Gall
Essential Family Chiropractic
30 S. 20th Ave. Unit E
Brighton, CO 80601
303-659-3128
essentialfamchiro@gmail.com

Drs. Marc and Lauren Nickens
Northgate Family Chiropractic
12245 Voyager Pkwy
Ste. 124
Colorado Springs, CO 80921
northgatefamilychiropractic.com

Drs. Ronil and Simone Pala
Mountain Valley Family
Chiropractic
115 E. Harmony Rd.
Ste. 200
Fort Collins CO 80525
Mountainvalleyml.com

FLORIDA
Seagate Chiropractic
3602 Madaca Lane
Tampa, FL 33618
813-217-3539

Dr. Jake Marshall
Marshall Family Chiropractic
7807 Baymeadows Rd E Suite 201
Jacksonville, FL
904-306-7777

GEORGIA
Dr. Fred Roberto & Dr. Anthony White
West Cobb Chiropractic
5941 Dallas Highway
Suite 500
Powder Springs GA 30127
770-919-7171

Dr. Alana Reisinger
Reisinger Family Chiropractic
1899 Powers Ferry Road SE
Ste. 170
Atlanta, GA 30339
770-627-5637
info@rfcatlanta.com

Dr. Tim Smith
True Source Family Chiropractic
11 Buford Village Way
Ste. 127
Buford GA 30518

IDAHO
Dr. Rosie Main
2300 W. Everest Ln
Suite 175 Meridian,
Idaho 83646
208-859-6170
DrMain.MaxLiving.com

ILLINOIS
Dr. Josh Johnson
Johnson Family Chiropractic
310 Susan Dr.
Suite 2
Normal, IL 61761
309-808-1123
www.drjohnson.maxliving.com/

Dr. James and Dr. Kalie Judge
Judge Family Chiropractic
2422 West Main St.
St. Charles, IL 60175
630-377-3500
Judgewellness@gmail.com

INDIANA
Dr. Leanne Schlueter
Greenwood Family Chiropractic
520 N State Road 135 Suite R
Greenwood, IN 46142
Info@greenwoodfamilychiropractic.com

IOWA

Dr. Abby Tebbe.
Health from Within of Dubuque
Dubuque, Iowa

Dr. Kevin Miller
E.P. True Chiropractic
1905 EP True Pkwy
#307
West Des Moines, IA 50265
515-309-3791

KANSAS

Dr. Jake Davidson
Davidson Family Chiropractic
7951 W. 160th St.
Ste.500
Overland Park, KS, 66223
www.davidsonfamilychiro.com

LOUISIANA

Dr. Antonio Rivera
Life by Design Chiropractic
2625 Dillard Loop, Suite C
Lake Charles, LA 70607
337-564-6197
www.lifebydesignchiropractic.
com

MICHIGAN

Dr. Bobby Belmonte
Woodland Family Chiropractic
3682 29th St SE
Suite A
Kentwood, MI 49512
616-288-4000

MINNESOTA

Dr. Brandon Buesgens
Becker Spine
13150 1st St.
Becker, MN 55308
BeckerSpineMN.com

Drs. Peter and Natalie Gianforte
Minnetonka Family Chiropractic
11349 Hwy 7
Minnetonka, MN 55305

Dr. Jeff McComb
Essential Health Chiropractic
1964 Rahncliff Court
Suite 100
Eagan, MN 55122
952-432-3833

Minnesota Family Chiropractic
7610 Lyndale Ave S
Ste. 600
Richfield, MN 55423
612.545.5672
Mnfamilychiropractic.com

Dr. Bria Spree
St. Paul Chiropractic
1575 7th St. W
Suite 101
St. Paul, MN 55102
www.stpaulchiropractic.com

MISSOURI
Dr. Nick Barnes
Health From Within Family
Chiropractic
9586 Manchester Rd.
St. Louis, MO 63119
314-942-8608
Healthfromwithinstl.com

Dr. Beth Barnes
Turning Point Chiropractic
14784 Manchester Rd.
Ballwin, MO 63011
MLturningpointchiropractic.com

MONTANA
Dr. Torrie Cheff
Adjusted 4 Life
Missoula, MT
406.552.7043

NEBRASKA
Dr. Jake Tucker
7011 Kentwell Ln.
#200
Lincoln, NE 68516
531.289.7100
GoodLifeFamilyChiropractic.
com

Dr. Matthew Matt Dietz
Discover Health Chiropractic
5815 Council St. NE
Ste. A-1
Cedar Rapids, Iowa 52402
319-393-1555
discoverhealthiowa.com

NEW JERSEY
Dr. Daniel Eleuteri
Invictus Family Chiropractic
276 E. Main St.
Denville, NJ 07834
973-627-0475
InvictusFamilyChiropractic.com

NORTH CAROLINA

Family Healing Chiropractic
7245 Pineville-Matthews Rd
Suite 300
Charlotte NC 28226
704-540-0055

Dr. Kristine Schmierer
Inspire Family Chiropractic
1636 Sardis Road, Suite 130
Charlotte, NC 28270

Drs. Jake & Christi Shuppe
Freedom Family Chiropractic
1330 5th Avenue
Suite 130
Garner, NC 27529
919-205-9990
freedomfamilychiro.com

OHIO

Dr. Ryan Berlin
Align Chiropractic
8039 Cincinnati Dayton Road
West Chester, Ohio 45069
513.571.1387
Drryan@alignhealthcenter.com

OKLAHOMA

Dr. Shawna Ortiz
Frontier Family Chiropractic
6444 NW Expressway
Suite 828A
Oklahoma City, OK 73132
405-470-6415

Dr. Brad Montgomery
Axis Chiropractic
www.Axischiroduncan.com
817 W Walnut Ave
Duncan Ok. 73533
580-467-2388

PENNSYLVANIA

Drs. Greg and Krysta O'Neill
Lititz Family Chiropractic
766 Lititz Pike
Lititz, PA 17543
Lititzfamilychiropractic@gmail.
com

Dr. Jason Kistler
Align Chiropractic
477 Lancaster Ave
Ste. 106
Malvern, PA 19355
AlignPA.com
484-318-7921

SOUTH CAROLINA
Dr. Brian Class
Life Essentials Health Center
www.lifeessentialshealth.com
843-284-8410
1501 Hwy 17
North Unit H
Mount Pleasant, SC 29464

Dr. Tom Stetson
Columbia Family Chiropractic
224 O'Neil Ct. #21
Columbia, SC 29229
803-788-8831
www.CFCforHealth.com

Darrah Family Chiropractic
1791 Woodruff Rd.
Greenville SC, 29607
864-254-9915

Dr. Sarah Losby
Capital city chiropractic
Columbia, SC 29212
803-708-4258
ccc.maxliving.com

TENNESSEE
Dr. Audra Arstikaitis
Innate Wellness
256 Germantown Bend CV
Suite 103
Cordova, TN 38018
901.737.3040

Dr. Eric Wright
Peak Family Health
1510 Gunbarrel Rd
Suite 600
Chattanooga TN 37421

Drs. Michael & Cassie Major
Major Family Chiropractic
2000 Richard Jones Rd
Ste. 150
Nashville, TN 37215
Info@MajorFamilyChiropractic.
com

Dr. Brittany Tinker
Tinker Family Chiropractic
12908 Lebanon Rd
Mt Juliet, TN 37122
(615) 287-2671
info@tinkerfamilychiropractic.
com

TEXAS

Dr. Brent Smith
Smith Family Chiropractic
www.drsmith.maxliving.com
5501 Hwy 290 west
Austin, TX 78735
512-915-1413

Dr. Aaron Wall
Gateway Chiropractic
3250 Hulen Street
Ste. 140
Ft. Worth, TX 76107
817-886-7545

Dr. Peter Martinez
Dr. Cody Capeloto
River City Wellness
8708 S. Congress Ave.
Suite 570
Austin, TX 78745
512-535-4500
Rivercitywellness.com

Dr. Krystal Barnett
Extraordinary Health &
Wellness Center
2930 Preston Rd
Ste. 120
Frisco, TX 75034
214-436-5420
extraordinaryhealthandwellness@
gmail.com

Dr. Bryan Henss
Clairton Family Chiropractic
3848 N. Tarrant Parkway
Ste. 130
Ft. Worth TX 76244
817-281-1400

Dr. Elise Hernandez
Vitality Family Chiropractic
3701 S. Cooper St.
Unit 185
Arlington, TX 76015
817-962-0182
www.VitalityChiroArlington.
com

Dr. Rob Neuenschwander
Neu Life Chiropractic
28105 Tomball Pkwy, #106A
Tomball, TX 77375

Dr. Meier Miller
Restoration Dallas Chiropractic
1152 N. Buckner Blvd
Ste. 100B
Dallas, TX 75218
www.restorationdallas.com
469-941-4899

Dr. Cody Capeloto
River City Wellness
8708 S. Congress Ave
Ste. 570
Austin, TX 78745

Dr. Rick Royston
Chase Oaks Chiropractic
305 W. Spring Creek Pkwy 104B
Plano, TX
75023 469-543-6999
drroyston.maxliving.com

Dr. Yaxaira Almeida Lopez
Momentum Family Chiropractic
613 Uptown Blvd
Suite 106
Cedar Hill, TX 75104
469-454-5100

WISCONSIN
Dr. Aaron Arfstrom
Apex Chiropractic
6053 Sandstone Rd
Eau Claire, WI 54701
715-834-2739

CANADA
Dr. Lianne Coombe
Abundant Health Chiropractic
34 McMurray Street
Brantford Ontario Canada
N3T 1W4
519-304-8994

Dr. Chantalle Goring
Inner Strength Family
Chiropractic & Wellness
2314 Arlington Ave
Saskatoon, SK Canada S7J 3L3
306-477-7799
innerstrengthfamilychiro@gmail.
com

Dr. Colin Elkin
160 Brant Ave.
Brantford ON, Canada
N3T 3H7
519-751-1154

ABOUT THE AUTHOR

Dr. Dan Eleuteri is a Chiropractor and Doctor of Functional Medicine. He is passionate about bringing God's laws and principles about health and healing to the world. Dr. Dan loves being able to share these truths to people all over the country with his speaking engagements. He has a private practice located in Denville, NJ. He has been featured on *The Rachael Ray Show*. He lives with his wife Lauren, their son Jack, and a new addition set to arrive in September 2020 in Morris County, New Jersey.

CAN YOU HELP?

Thank You For Reading My Book!

*I really appreciate all of your feedback,
and I love hearing what you have to say.
I need your input to make the next version
of this book and my future books better.*

*Please leave me an honest review on Amazon
letting me know what you thought of the book.*

*Thanks so much!
Dr. Dan Eleuteri*

Want Dr. Dan to come and speak at your church or place of business?
Need individual or group coaching? Contact us at:
DRDAN.ELEUTERI@GMAIL.COM

Made in the USA
Middletown, DE
27 August 2020